Tina Brice

Buying Goods and Servic

GW00393444

a professional guide
to contracting
including
model conditions

THE
CHARTERED INSTITUTE OF
PURCHASING & SUPPLY

AD Allwright/ RW Oliver
Revised by ES Singleton
and KR Burnett

Acknowledgement

The authors' acknowledgements and thanks are due to members of the CIPS Legal Committee for their advice and encouragement, and to the CIPS Secretariat.

This revised edition incorporates amendments and additions made by Mrs E.S. Singleton LL.B, Solicitor and Principal in Singleton's, Solicitors, of Pinner Hill, Middlesex, designed to reflect changes in the law affecting buyer and seller, since publication of the 1993 edition. Mrs Singleton would like to thank her clients and especially her family who have grown used to weekends arranged around legal writing.

In particular, reference is made in this revised edition to new rules on exclusion of liability and consumer contracts, to the Sale of Goods Amendment Act 1994 and the Arbitration Act 1996, as well as to recent rulings on retention of title and product liability. A new section on competition law is included.

Material in this edition is intended to provide general guidance, and does not claim to be authoritative in relation to the present law or to its interpretation. Those seeking such direction should consult professional advisers.

The Editors

E. Susan Singleton, LL.B. Solicitor is principal of Singletons Solicitors and advises clients on commercial, competition, computer/IT and intellectual property law. She is editor of *Purchasing and Supply Briefing* and *Trading Law* and author of several books in this field. She is a member of the Institute of Export, the Competition Law Association and the Licensing Executive Society.
Singletons, The Ridge, South View Road, Pinner Hill, Middlesex HA2 0ND.
Telephone 0181 866 1934. Fax. 0181 429 9212. E Mail essingleton@link.org.

K.R. Burnett, BA, MA is Technical Services Officer with The Chartered Institute of Purchasing and Supply. He has produced a number of reports and bibliographies for CIPS Bookshop, and has written articles and book reviews for *Supply Management* and other specialist journals.

Contents

Part One: Buying Strategy

Part Two: Contract Strategy Planning, Award and Administration

Part Three: Model Conditions of Contract

Preface

The excitement and challenge that surrounds the involvement in Purchasing and Contracting is due in no small measure to the constant changes that take place in legislation at home, in the EU, and further afield. In addition, the pressure exerted on the Buyer to contribute to his organisation's commercial progress, or indeed survival, brings an ever-increasing requirement to understand and negotiate terms and conditions of contract that will protect these objectives.

Consequently, the authors of "Contracting for Goods and Services" first published in 1986 and the Chartered Institute of Purchasing and Supply have responded to these changes and have updated the advice given in that publication by expanding the guidance in many topics including "Quality", "Product Liability", "Warranties", "Post-Tender Negotiation" and "Retention of Title".

The similarity in the thought processes associated with "purchasing" and "contracting" produces demands from students and the more mature persons engaged in these professions, especially those in smaller organisations, for a simple guide explaining the intricate decision-making that can safeguard the buyer's firm or organisation.

The book is published, therefore, in three parts as before: Part 1 explains the philosophy behind both areas whilst Part 2 delves into the more complex area of contracting; Part 3 combines the two areas and provides a series of model conditions, purposely restricted to the major areas of risk from which buying organisations require protection. These Conditions are amplified with Notes for Guidance, which precede the model clauses, and which should be consulted before starting to draft a particular contract.

The authors have retained the same objectives as the Institute's previous edition, ie to provide a guide to buyers in their efforts to establish trading terms that are fair to both Buyers and Sellers alike and to complement the syllabus content of the CIPS examinations relating to Purchasing and Contracting.

A word of warning, however, to those buyers in the public services, Government Departments and other organisations bound by commercial disciplines regulated by EU or GATT procedures. The tendering regulations adopted by countries in the European Union in relation to public procurement require specific administrative knowledge, guidance for which should be sought.

While the authors have based the advice contained in this book on their best knowledge and experience, neither they nor the publishers accept legal liability of any kind in respect of the application of that advice.

Preface to Fourth Edition

Since the first edition of this book was published, sale of goods law has developed quite substantially. The concept of "merchantable quality" has been replaced by "satisfactory" quality, the general product safety regulations and Unfair Terms in Consumer Contracts Regulations have come into force, the Arbitration Act 1996 is in effect and public procurement law has altered, in particular with the implementation of the Utilities Directive.

This edition also includes a new section on competition law — both UK and EU which has a considerable impact on buying goods and services and on agency and distribution law.

Use of "he" in this book includes "she". (Many purchasing managers are female). This fourth edition is up to date as at 1st August 1997. Whilst every effort has been made to ensure the accuracy of the text the publishers, authors and editor cannot accept liability for any loss occasioned by reliance on this book. In particular the book is not a substitute for independent legal advice from a solicitor and readers are recommended to seek such advice when necessary.

Introduction

The Confusion of Buying v Contracting

What is "Buying"? ... What is "Purchasing"? ... What is "Contracting"? ... Is there any difference in these activities? Why do we refer sometimes to the "the Buyer" or "the Purchaser" or "the Supplies Officer" or "the Client" or "the Employer" or "the Authority" or "the Hirer"? Also, why do we have the "Seller" or the "Supplier" or the "Contractor"?

Why is there sometimes a "Purchase Order" or "Contract Order" or a "Purchase Agreement" or a "Supplies Order" or, sometimes, just plain "Contract"?

Why is the paperwork sometimes a single sheet, but in other instances several volumes of schedules and documents?

Let us try to dispel the confusion and tell you what this book is all about ...

When one party is prepared to pay another party for the supply of goods or services, however simple or complex, then, subject to the comments and advice referred to in this book, the parties enter into a "Contract". Unfortunately, owing to the varying circumstances and customs in organisations, private industry and public sector operations, together with different levels of experience and attitudes in their commercial departments, there is no standardisation in terminology.

However, it is generally safe to assume that for the purchase of an "off the shelf" item, where the Specification, Programme, Price and Conditions of Contract require a minimum description and the risk is low, then it is not unusual to evidence the "Contract" on a "Purchase Order" or similarly described document.

At the other extreme, a multi-million pound contract for an extensive plant construction will require detailed documentation covering all aspects of the rights and obligations of both parties to the contract. Obviously the latter example takes much more time to establish the complete negotiation, but it is a dangerous practice to cut corners in an attempt to "get into bed" with a supplier or contractor quickly by issuing a "Purchase Order" or, even worse, a Letter of Intent. The commercial world is strewn with evidence of costly delays in delivery and completion caused by naive demonstrations of haste at the pre-contract stage.

Consequently this book sets out to convince you that there is no fundamental difference between PURCHASING and CONTRACTING. The "thought procedure" should be exactly the same when you are establishing a contract that will be evidenced by a PURCHASE ORDER or a full blown CONTRACT.

Part One: Buying Strategy

Before the buyer enters into a contract there are certain important aspects to be clarified, all of which will have a bearing on the conditions to be applied to the contract, eg what are the financial considerations – price stability – terms of payment – suppliers' vulnerability? Is the source of supply from outside the United Kingdom? How critical is the delivery date?

The object of Part One is to bring to the buyer's attention some of the major points which require a decision, and to provide a background upon which such decisions can be based.

The guidance given in Part One, whilst covering the basic principles, is most relevant to contracts for the sale of goods or to supply-and-install contracts having a minor element of site work. Guidance on the wider aspects of major capital contracts will be found by reference to Part Two.

Where additions or amendments to the Model Standard Conditions detailed in Part Three are prescribed, or are drawn up by the buyer, these should be set out in full in the purchase order as 'Special Conditions' or incorporated into the Model Standard Conditions. Care must be taken to ensure that such changes are consistent with the standard conditions, and that no ambiguities are created. The same words must be used to describe the same item or activity; if the buyer uses two different words he will be assumed to have done so deliberately, and therefore they have different meanings.

1 Contractual obligations

1.1 Why have conditions of contract?

Contract law is that branch of the law which determines whether a promise between two parties is legally enforceable and what the legal consequences are should either party fail to keep its promise.

Normally business is conducted on a goodwill basis. Generally the seller is looking to future business and the buyer, for his part, expects his requirements to be serviced in a prompt and efficient manner.

Any disputes are usually resolved by the parties sitting down together and talking the problems through. However, disputes can arise in all manner of ways and the terms and conditions agreed at the time of contracting form the ground rules against which such disputes can be discussed and resolved.

Failure to establish properly the terms of a contract would mean that the transaction would be conducted under common law and any default could result in the insolvency or bankruptcy of the defaulting party since damages could be unlimited where losses are huge.

Thus both parties are looking for some basic protection to cover the eventuality of an unresolvable dispute or a justifiable claim for damages. In the event of a dispute being referred to the courts the judge is **not** empowered to make the contract for the parties. He may only interpret the intention of the parties at the time the contract was formed, assess the action or lack of action of the parties within the framework of their agreement and, having regard to all relevant legislation, give a decision based on those facts.

1.2 The basic ingredients

The law provides that there should be seven basic ingredients of a contract:

Intention − both parties must enter into a contract with the intention that legal consequences would arise if either party defaulted.

Offer and acceptance − one party must have made an offer to the other and that offer must have been accepted.

Consideration − a contract is basically a form of exchange: one party receiving in exchange for performing his promise something (generally money) from the other party.

Contractual capacity − generally any person or company of whatever nationality or sex may enter into a binding contract. However, special rules apply for the protection of minors, insane persons, and other people of whom advantage could be taken.

Genuineness of consent − consent, to be bound by the terms of the contract, must not have been obtained by fraud, deceit, duress or misrepresentation whether deliberate or unintentional.

Legality −the contract must not be entered into for an illegal or immoral purpose.

1.3 The force of law

When one person or firm sells goods or services to another, the rights and duties of both parties are governed by their contract, **but** the contents of the contract are, themselves, the subject of various legislative provisions.

Until the end of the 19th century the rule of *caveat emptor* (let buyer beware) prevailed. This was substantially modified in 1893 by the Sale of Goods Act which laid down a range of conditions that were to be implied, according to the circumstances, into every contract for the sale of goods. However, it was always open to the seller expressly to contract out of his statutory liability. This brought about a situation where often goods could be bought only if the buyer was willing to give up his rights in law.

The implied rights are:
Proper title − the buyer is entitled to be sure that the seller has the right to sell the goods.

Sale by description – where there is a contract for the sale of goods by description the goods shall correspond with that description.

Fitness for purpose – the goods shall be fit for the purpose intended where such purpose has been made known to the seller.

Satisfactory quality – where the seller sells goods in the ordinary course of business the buyer can expect the goods to be of a standard that a reasonable person would regard as satisfactory taking account of any description of the goods, the price (if relevant) and all other relevant circumstances.

Clauses reducing these implied rights became known as 'exclusion clauses', a typical example being:

> 'No representation, warranty, condition or term, express or implied, statutory or otherwise as to the quality of the product, its fitness for any purpose or compliance with any sample or description or in any other respect shall apply to this contract or to any delivery made hereunder'.

Such unreasonable clauses were rendered invalid in the case of 'consumer' sales under the provisions of the Sale of Goods (Implied Terms) Act 1973. This protection was extended into contracts for services by the Unfair Contract Terms Act 1977. The 1893 Act had been further amended by the Misrepresentation Act 1967; thus given all these amendments it became very difficult, without cross-referencing statutes, to find out which portion of what Act applied to certain circumstances. The situation was clarified by the passing of the Sales of Goods Act 1979 which repealed the 1893 Act and embodies the amendments into one statute: not new law but an easier situation to handle.

The Supply of Goods and Services Act 1982 had the effect of implying into contracts for the supply of goods which are not contracts of sale or hire-purchase, (eg supply and install contracts) terms of satisfactory quality and fitness for purpose, thus placing such contracts on a par with those governed by the Sale of Goods Act 1979.

Until the 1982 Act there had been no general statute concerned with service contracts (window cleaning, maintenance work, etc.). However, the law now requires that:

i   where no specific time has been agreed before the contract is made, the work must be done within a reasonable time;

ii if no specific charge has been agreed before the contract is made, then the price must be a reasonable one;

iii the work must be performed with reasonable care and skill.

The application of the 1973, 1979 and 1982 Acts can be summarised as follows:

Sale of Goods (Implied Terms) Act 1973	:	Hire-purchase deals.
Sale of Goods Act 1979	:	Sale of goods, including credit sales and conditional sales.
Supply of Goods and Services Act 1982	:	Hire or lease arrangements. Barter trading. Labour-plus-materials contracts. Service contracts.
Consumer Protection Act 1987	:	Redress against supplier of defective goods.

The Unfair Contract Terms Act 1977 is not concerned with the imposition of obligations upon the seller; it is relevant only where an obligation is imposed elsewhere, either by statute or by common law, and the seller seeks to exclude that obligation. In addition to providing the buyer with protection as regards his 'implied rights' the 1977 Act also protects the buyer against the seller seeking to avoid liability for negligence, breach of contract, etc., by providing that:

i a person cannot by reference to any contract term exclude or restrict his liability for death or personal injury resulting from negligence;

ii in the case of other loss or damage, a person cannot so exclude or restrict his liability for negligence except insofar as the term satisfies the test of reasonableness;

iii when a contracting party is in breach of contract he cannot exclude or restrict any liability of his in respect of the breach, or claim to be entitled to render a contractual performance substantially different from that which was reasonably expected of him, or, in respect of the whole or any part of his contractual obligation, to render no performance at all, except insofar as the contract term satisfies the test of reasonableness.

Exclusion clauses will be valid for business to business sales only if the courts decide that they meet the 'test of reasonableness'. In deciding whether it is fair and reasonable to exclude any of the implied conditions, regard must be paid to all the circumstances and in particular to the following matters:

− the strength of the bargaining position of the parties, taking into account suitable alternative products and sources of supply;

− whether the buyer received an inducement to agree to the exclusion term;

- whether the buyer knew or ought to have known of the existence and extent of the exclusion term;

- where the exclusion term arises from the non-performance of some condition, whether it is reasonable to expect that compliance with the condition would be practicable;

- whether the goods were manufactured, processed or adapted to the special order of the buyer.

The 1977 Act applies as regards unreasonable exclusion clauses in those cases where the contract is on standard terms, or is a consumer contract. If the exclusion clause has been negotiated between the parties then the 1977 Act may not in fact apply. It is therefore always prudent to seek legal advice.

Consumer Contracts

The Unfair Terms in Consumer Contracts Regulations 1994 (SI 1994/3159) implemented the EU Unfair Terms Directive 93/13. All EU member states are obliged to have similar legislation. The Regulations apply to sales to consumers. The Unfair Contract Terms Act 1977 described above continues in full force and effect (with the 1994 Regulations running alongside covering similar ground) but only applying to sales to consumers. The 1977 Act applies to exclusion and limitation clauses. The 1994 Regulations render void any "unreasonable" (rather than "unfair", - the term used in the 1977 Act) clause in a contract with a consumer. Thus the 1994 Regulations apply potentially to any clause in a contract, not just to exclusion clauses.

Under the 1977 Regulations a term will be unfair where it causes a significant imbalance in the parties' rights and obligations arising under the contract to the detriment of the consumer, and is contrary to the requirement of good faith. Complete legal textbooks have been written on the subject of what is "good faith"; however to assist the person drafting a contract, an annex to the Regulations contains an indicative list of terms which are unfair. Those drafting contracts with consumers may care to note that the 1994 Regulations are available from the Stationery Office; the Office of Fair Trading, which has an Unfair Terms Unit, is also a useful source of advice. The Unit has published three detailed Reports and a set of Guidance Notes on the 1994 Regulations giving many examples of terms which the OFT has determined to be unfair. This is a very useful source of information on the types of wording to be used in such clauses. The Reports and Notes are available free of charge from the OFT.

However, most purchasing managers will be buying on behalf of a company and the 1994 Regulations are not therefore relevant because they apply only to consumer transactions. Therefore it is the 1977 Act which is of most relevance. One difficulty in practice is whether the purchaser should accept a very one-sided exclusion clause knowing or suspecting that it would be held to be void under the 1977 Act as it is "unreasonable". This is a risky strategy for the buyer for several reasons. If the buyer seeks to argue that a clause is void because it is unreasonable then court proceedings have to be launched. This can be very expensive - probably well over £10,000 for a High Court action. Also only about 5% of court actions started result in a hearing in court. Most are settled out of court with compromise on both sides, so the buyer may end up paying all his own costs as part of the settlement.

Generally it is better to ensure that the exclusion clause is amended so that it is acceptabe to both parties rather than relying on the hope that it might be void. It is common for a buyer to agree to an exclusion of consequential losses in a supplier's exclusion clauses though not all buyers are prepared to do this. However buyers who agree they cannot sue the supplier for loss of profit and related consequential losses should check carefully that their insurance policies cover them against such losses. The buyer who accepts an exclusion of consequential loss should ensure there is some scope to sue the supplier for losses which directly flow from a breach of the contract and that the overall limit on all claims brought by the buyer against the seller is not too low. A figure limiting liability to two or three times the contract price is better for the buyer than a limit of the price itself. Sometimes a particular figure is chosen such as £25,000, £500,000 or for some larger value contracts, £1m or £2m. Often a contract provides that the supplier must have insurance cover of a particular amount and that the supplier must show the policy to the buyer on demand. Much depends on how much power the buyer has in negotiating the contract. Some buyers are able to stipulate that the supplier is responsible for all reasonably foreseeable losses flowing from a breach of contract - thus there is no limit on the overall amount which can be claimed (provided the amount of the losses claimed can be proven) and there is then no exclusion of consequential loss either. Conversely some buyers are unable to negotiate any changes to the supplier's contract at all.

In St Albans v ICL (a Court of Appeal decision in 1996) the court declared ICL's limitation of liability to £100,000 in its standard terms void. This was because the clause was an unreasonable exclusion of liability under the Unfair Contract Terms Act 1977. Normally the 1977 Act can only be used for consumer contracts and contracts on standard terms and ICL's conditions had been heavily negotiated by St Albans Council; however the court said that as the exclusion clause remained much as it was in the original standard terms and was "effectively unchanged" this was indeed a contract on standard terms and therefore potentially subject to challenge under the 1977 Act. In particular ICL had insurance cover of £50m and was part of a much bigger group than the small local council.

Therefore in all the circumstances the limitation of liability to £100,000 was unreasonable and could not be enforced. St Albans was able to recover just under £1m of its losses.

1.4 When is a contract formed?

Many orders are preceded by a series of meetings between the buyer and the seller, settling specifications, approving samples, establishing prices, etc. Unless these discussions or negotiations are conducted with care, the parties can find themselves contracted orally, so that the subsequent order becomes merely a document for accountancy purposes. During these discussions and with the enthusiasm of concluding a deal there is a real danger of creating a legally binding contract. (Contracts for the supply of goods and services do not have to be in writing to be legally enforceable).

Another important point to bear in mind as far as contracts are concerned is that any limitation placed on an individual's power to commit his company is purely an administrative device and would not affect the validity of the oral contract unless that is the other party knew of the limitation. Unless care is taken during the negotiation, binding oral contracts in excess of one's limits of authority — either on the part of the buyer or, as is equally important, on the part of the seller — can easily be created.

On the other hand many orders, especially for standard components, are placed without prior negotiation. They are acknowledged by the seller, the goods are delivered, the invoice is passed for payment, and then something is discovered with respect to the goods which is not quite as expected. On questioning the seller, the buyer is referred to seller's conditions of sale. The order, it transpires, had not been acknowledged and the buyer finds himself faced with a conflict of conditions. To create a contract there must be an offer and an unqualified acceptance of that offer. Unfortunately, in practice, many transactions take place without these formalities having been completed.

When the buyer's order is the offer, the seller's acknowledgement, if unqualified, that is, it does not differ in any material way from the details of the order, constitutes the acceptance, and a contract exists between the parties. However, if the acknowledgement of order shows that the seller intends his own conditions to apply then this constitutes a counter-offer and no contract exists at that point. A statement on the order excluding the seller's conditions is no protection for the buyer and does not legally affect the counter-offer situation. This aspect is particularly important where acknowledgements are handled by persons other than the originator of the order. Always check for a possible conflict of conditions.

The acceptance of an offer must be unequivocal or it may operate as a counter-offer. It must match the terms of the offer and be unconditional. Silence may not be presumed to mean acceptance. The effect of counter-offers is most important and tends to be either ignored or misunderstood in business life.

A counter-offer operates as a rejection of the original offer. Thus each counter-offer constitutes a new ballgame — one cannot go back to the original offer without it being re-offered. An offer may be accepted by conduct, eg by despatching goods in response to an offer to purchase (an order) without prior acknowledgement of the order. Similarly, an offer to supply goods made by the seller (this offer may be in the form of a counter-offer to the buyer's order), can be accepted by the buyer by the latter taking delivery of, and using, the goods. Where a contract has been formed by conduct it is often difficult to say exactly what terms have been agreed. The buyer may find himself bound by the seller's conditions.

It follows, therefore, that it is desirable that every contractual arrangement should be made by means of a clear offer and an equally clear and matching acceptance so that the actual terms of the contract can be readily identified.

Post-contract negotiations cannot affect the terms of the contract unless those negotiations themselves result in an offer and an acceptance constituting a contract, the intention being to amend the previous contract.

The existence of a contract does not necessarily mean that all of the obligations of the buyer and seller have been fully specified at the time of forming the contract. There are instances such as variation orders, or change control provisions where, under the terms of the contract themselves, the work can be varied in accordance with procedures set out in the contract.

There is a situation, however, where the roles of seller and buyer are, to a degree, reversed. This is where an enquiry and a tender are involved. An enquiry is not an offer, it is an invitation to do business (in legal terms 'to treat'). The seller's tender is the offer and the buyer's order is the acceptance.

Providing the terms of the tender and the order agree there is a contract, and an acknowledgement of such an order is merely a courtesy and cannot affect the contract. It follows therefore that, where a tender and an order have been exchanged and a contract formed, neither party is free to introduce new terms as they would be if the negotiations were still in progress.

Another instance of where the validity of a contract depends on offer and acceptance is the Call-off Contract, sometimes referred to as a

Standing Arrangement, a Standing Offer, or, in relation to contracts subject to the requirements of the EU Procurement Supplies, Works, Utilities and Remedies Directives, a Framework Agreement.

Such an arrangement allows goods, or in some cases services, to be ordered or called-off as required during the period of the arrangement. Such arrangements are often made by a central buying organisation on behalf of users which may or may not be part of the same organisation. They are essentially enabling agreements between an organisation and supplier, which specify terms and conditions of contract, discounts available, ordering, acceptance, and bill-paying procedures.

Such an arrangement only becomes contractually binding when the call-off order is in accordance with the terms and conditions of the call-off arrangement, has been accepted by the supplier, and consideration between the parties has been agreed. Where such arrangements are operated by public sector bodies and certain national utilities they may be subject to the rules governing public purchasing in the European Community, and to the Agreement on Government Procurement (GPA) of GATT (General Agreement on Tariffs and Trade). Guidance can be obtained by referring to the relevant CIPS, DTI and HM Treasury publications.

1.5 How is a contract discharged?
Assuming that the basic ingredients for the formation of a Contract referred to in paragraph 1.2 above are present and there is a valid contract — how can it be discharged?

There are a number of ways:

i By performance:
   Most "one-off" contracts are discharged by performance — by doing what was agreed — eg delivering the goods ordered, etc.

ii By release:
   In some circumstances one party may agree to release the other party from his obligations, but there should either be some consideration for this or technically the agreement to release should be executed as a deed.

iii Substituted contract:
   The parties may terminate one contract by substituting a new one. It is sometimes difficult to distinguish between an amendment made to an old contract, and the substitution of a new contract.

iv Intervening circumstances:
   Where circumstances, beyond the reasonable control of the parties, occur such that the contract becomes impossible to perform (eg acts of God, fire, war or civil disturbance) — the common term for such

occurrences being *force majeure* − the party directly affected by such circumstances may be relieved of some or all of his obligations under the contract. Contracts often contain a clause to identify the circumstances and set out the remedies.

v Time:
Sometimes it is made an essential term of a contract that it must be performed by a certain time; an example is a clause stipulating that time is of the essence of the contract (see paragraph 5.3 page 36). If such a condition is not complied with, the injured party may treat the contract as at an end; depending on the contract and surrounding circumstances, he may be able to sue for breach of contract.

vi Termination:
Some contracts, particularly contracts for services rather than goods, contain a clause covering notice provisions for termination, eg 'either party may terminate this agreement by giving to the other party three months' written notice of his intention to terminate this contract'.

vii Bankruptcy or insolvency:
As many firms know to their cost, an order for discharge in a bankruptcy or insolvency may be made whereby all debts and liabilities provable in the bankruptcy or insolvency may be released, ie the bankrupt person or insolvent firm may be discharged from his/its obligations − thereby putting an abrupt end to a contract.

1.6 Disputes and their resolution

It is not uncommon during the execution of contracts for the purchase of materials or services for a 'dispute' to arise between the parties. The dispute may be triggered by a difference of opinion of what is meant by terminology in a specification or other contractual documentation, or subsequent instructions given to the supplier or contractor. Sometimes the dispute centres on the non-acceptability of work performed.

In all cases the parties have to settle their differences themselves or have them settled by others. So there are three alternatives:

− the negotiating table

− arbitration

− the courts

Recourse to arbitration or the courts is extremely expensive and very time-consuming and in the majority of cases by the time that the true cost of preparing and presenting evidence is ascertained even the 'winner' cannot be satisfied with the result.

Whilst the Arbitration Act 1996, in force since 1997, sought to improve matters, only time will tell whether it improves the previous position. It is worth noting however that small arbitration claims can be settled within a few months from the date of notification to the Chartered Institute of Arbitrators.

This book has been written with the firm conviction that arbitration clauses should not be included in UK contracts on the basis that, as disputes would have to await settlement in the courts, the parties would be more amenable to settling their differences around the negotiating table. Arbitration is formal and usually solicitors and barristers are instructed. It can be slower and more costly than the courts, but unlike court proceedings is confidential.

However, modern commercial practice is making increasing use of new methods of resolving contractual disputes without the need for costly and prolonged litigation or formal aribtration procedures. One such technique gaining increasing support is the use of Alternative Disputes Resolution (ADR) whereby trained mediators, knowledgeable and experienced in the technical aspects of the particular contract, will attempt to arrive at a solution with the aid of, and acceptable to, the parties. Further information on the use of ADR can be obtained by reference to the Chartered Institute of Arbitrators and other professional organisations active in the area of contracting, including the Centre for Alternative Dispute Resolution.

Buying from abroad however sometimes requires a different attitude and in such cases, aribtration can help as described in section 9, page 55 *et seq.*

1.7 Warranty

A warranty is a term of contract subsidiary to the main purpose of the contract, a breach of which would give rise only to a claim for damages and not to a right to repudiate the contract.

By evolution, in contracts of sale, the word *Warranty* has come to mean the extent of the obligations that the seller is prepared to accept in the event that the goods sold are subsequently found to be, or become, defective. It also relates to the period during which he is prepared to be bound by those obligations.

The decision as to what liabilities they seek to exclude will usually be taken by the buyer and the seller in the light of the commercial circumstances. However, the extent to which the contracting parties can seek to reduce or exclude their contractual liability by the use of notices, disclaimers or exclusion clauses is governed by the Unfair Contract Terms Act 1977 and 1994 Regulations. (See paragraph 1.3, pages 12-13)

The warranty clause provided in the model standard conditions detailed in Part 3 does not reflect the full legal rights available to the Buyer, nor the full legal obligations of the Seller, under the legislation relating to Sale of Goods, Supply of Goods and Services, and Unfair Contract Terms; rather, it is a pragmatic attempt to establish a reasonable position acceptable to both parties, with the practical objective of arriving at a workable agreement.

The waranty clause therefore voluntarily limits the claim by the buyer, in the event of goods proving faulty in use for reasons other than misuse, to restoration of the goods to full working order, or the replacement of the goods, plus damages to the full value of the purchase order under which the goods were obtained. The buyer voluntarily gives up any claim to damages for loss of profit; however, costs of dismantling and reinstallation and making good resulting damage to surrounding equipment and property are included, subject to the buyer's legal obligation to minimise his loss.

The objective is to restore the buyer's position to that at the time he placed the purchase order and not necessarily to place him, financially, in the position in which he would have been had the contract been properly performed. However some buyers would prefer the latter and should modify the clause accordingly.

In addition to defining the legal liabilities, there are the practical aspects of the operation of the warranty to be considered. It is important for the buyer to establish exactly what is covered by the warranty, for example:

- does the warranty only cover the return of the defective goods to the seller's premises and does the buyer have to pay the cost of carriage? (Depending on the size of the goods and the distances to be travelled, carriage can be expensive;

- is there any commitment on the part of the seller as regards response time — would the buyer be happy if it took say, twelve months to rectify or replace the defective goods?

- does the warranty clause cover a visit by the seller's service organisation to the buyer's premises. If so, does it cover all costs, ie callout charges, parts and labour?

- again, response times are probably important to the buyer, and what if the buyer needs a response outside of normal working hours (during the night, Saturday, Sunday, and Bank Holidays)? Buyers should make sure there is a call out time **and** a time in which a fault will be fixed.

If the service visit is included in the warranty, it is important to remember all the aspects associated with contractors visiting and working on the buyer's premises (insurance, site rules and regulations, safety, security, etc).

Where the buyer is considering a maintenance contract (following the warranty period) it is well worth while negotiating the maintenance contract before placing the contract for the supply of the goods and to include the warranty period as part of the maintenance contract.

1.8 Competition Law

English law largely leaves buyer and seller free to determine with whom and how they will contract. However sometimes it intervenes, often through competition law. In the UK this is primarily the Restrictive Trade Practices Act 1976 (RTPA). This puts the Office of Fair Trading in charge of investigating anti-competitive agreements, cartels, price fixing, market sharing etc. Agreements which fall within the Act should be registered at the OFT and may be referred to the Restrictive Practices Court. The Court may make orders requiring the companies concerned not to make restrictive agreements again. Breach of those orders is contempt of court and can lead to fines or even jail sentences for directors and managers. A new UK Competition Bill was announced in 1997 so the law in this field may change; however it is likely to be significantly toughened in accordance with EU requirements (see below).

The Act does not just apply to cartels; all forms of co-operative contracts can be required to be registered. If they are not then the restrictions are void so cannot be enforced in court. The most common registered agreements are franchising contracts, company share and purchaser/share sale agreements and joint venture arrangements. The Act is complicated and legal advice should be sought in cases of doubt, but principally it applies where two parties to an agreement accept the two restrictions as to goods or services as set out in section 6 of sll of the Act. Restrictions caught include the persons to whom the contract goods will be resold or the terms on which they will be resold and any restrictions as to price. Where both parties have a joint UK group turnover of, (1997) £20m, then there is no requirement to register under the Act unless the agreement includes price restrictions. All contracts should be checked before signature to see whether they should be registered first. The OFT is willing to give views on agreement before signature and registration must take place within 3 months of the agreement beging signed. No restriction should come into force before registration.

The Act also has special provisions for trade associations - recommendations by associations, even if not binding on members must be registered, such as a recommendation not to buy from a particular person. Separately under s7 of the Act agreements for the exchange of information about prices or terms must be registered. Buyers often get caught out through entering into a tripartite arrangement, preferred supplier arrangements, consortium agreements and the like where restrictions may be included in the agreements and two or more parties accept a restriction to their commerial freedom.

Also relevant is the UK Resale Prices Act 1976 which prohibits minimum resale price maintenance by suppliers. No buyer should be told the price at which goods must be resold and it is unlawful to withhold supplies because of the buyer's resale pricing unless the very narrow special "loss leading' provisions of the 1976 Act apply. Recommended prices are allowed as long as they do not become a *de facto* resale price.

Other UK competition statutes are the Fair Trading Act 1973 which is not relevant to most buyers - certain mergers and monopolies may be referred to the Monopolies and Mergers Commission under the Act there is also the Competition Act 1980 which entitles the OFT and the MMC to investigate certain anti-competitive practices such as refusals to supply by dominant companies and unfair trading practices.

Additionally there are the EC competition rules in Articles 85 and 86 of the Treaty of Rome. Breach of these rules can lead to fines of 10% of group annual worldwide turnover. Article 85 prohibits anti-competitive agreements. Article 86 just applies to dominant companies - and prohibits an abuse of a dominant position. Dominance usually means at least 40% of the market, perhaps the whole EU or one of the larger states such as the UK. For commercial agreements breach of Article 85 is the most likely. Articles 85 and 86 only apply where the agreement may affect trade between member states but this is often the case even where both parties are in the UK. If the parties' joint market shares are under 5% **and** group annual turnover is under 300 million ECU then the European Commission believe the rules are unlikely to apply as the arrangement is *"de minimis"* - however those rules are set to change and in some areas markets are very narrowly defined. It is generally better to comply with the rules than take a chance by assuming they do not apply.

Obviously avoid entering into arrangements with competitors or other businesses either to partition markets, share customers, divide tenders or fix prices. For certain common types of contract where restrictions which might fall within Article 85 are common, such as exclusive distribution and purchasing arrangements, franchising, patent and knowhow licensing and joint research and development agreements, there are detailed EU regulations setting out what restrictions and clauses may be included in such contracts, as well as those which may not be included. As well as risking fines of up to 10% of turnover those breaking these rules will find that third parties may sue for damages and clauses which are restrictions in contracts will be void. This means they may have to proceed with a very different contract from that they intended to enter into originally - the rest of the contract is valid but the restrictions protecting their position are void.

Contracts can be submitted to the European Commission for individual exemption under Article 85(3) but there would be no point in notifying a cartel, for example, as no exemption would be given. Buyers who are suffering at the hands of a cartel or dominant supplier, or who are threatened with supplies being cut off should consider making a formal complaint to the European Commission and/or the cartels hotline at the OFT.

1.9 Intellectual Property

Buyers need to exercise particular caution where a contract involves the licensing of intellectual property such as patents, copyright, designs or trade marks. Such contracts are not clearly goods or services and thus the protection of such statutes as the Sale of Goods Act 1979 may not be available - the courts have not made a definitive decision on this issue. Therefore make sure contracts contain all express provisions required. For example, the supplier or licensor of the rights should warrant he owns the rights and can grant the licence and that it will indemnify the buyer licensee against all costs, losses and expenses arising from the license being sued for infringement of a third party's intellectual property rights in that which has been licensed to the buyer/licensee.

Those buying computer software should make reference to specialist reference works. They should also be aware of the range of Terms and Conditions of contract for the purchase of computer software available from the CIPS; these are listed on p.224.

It is worth mentioning here the "ownership" trap. Many of those having software or other copyright works specially made for them on a bespoke or commission basis assume they will own the underlying intellectual property rights as they have paid for them. In fact under the Copyright Designs and Patents Act 1988 the author or the author's employer owns the rights and all the person paying obtains is a right to use the works. That may be all the buyer wants; however the buyer cannot then stop the person writing the works from licensing them to third parties and thereby generating a useful income. The position under the 1988 Act can be altered by a simple contract term saying that all intellectual property rights in works generated through the contract will be owned by the "buyer/licensee" and making it clear what the buyer can or cannot do with the works after they have been supplied. In such cases it is recommended that legal guidance should be obtained from a specialist intellectual property solicitor.

1.10 Agency and Distribution

Finally, where goods are bought through a buying agent the provisions of the Commercial Agents (Council Directive) Regulations 1993 (SI 1993/3053) should be borne in mind. These Regulations give substantial rights to agents who buy or sell goods on behalf of a "principal".

The provisions of the Regulations in particular as to compensation payable to agents on termination of the agreement cannot be varied by contract, so careful thought must be given to whether or not to dispense with an agent's service. Any such decision should be based on sound legal advice. The DTI have issued guidance notes on the Regulations and in 1996 the European Commission issued a report on the compensation and indemnity provisions of the Agency Directive on which the Regulations are based. Certain of the provisions of the Directive can be modified or improved by contractual provisions so contracts need to be drafted with care. The Regulations provide minimum periods of notice to terminate an agency contract - up to three months for agents in their second and subsequent years of service. They also specify when and how commission is payable as well as the circumstances in which compensation or an indemnity is payable. In relation to the latter, advice should be sought from a solicitor specialising in this area before notice of termination is given.

A distributor is distinguished from an agent because they own the goods they market and then resell them. An agent never has title to the goods, his function being to find customers - the contract of sale is between the supplier and the customer usually with the agent paid a percentage commission. There is no specific distribution law in the UK. Under EC competition law distribution agreements must be carefully drawn up to comply with the detailed EC regulations in this field. In particular although a distributor may be prevented by a contract term from advertising outside his area he must not be prohibited absolutely from making sales outside his area otherwise large fines will be levied by the European Commission. Fines of millions of pounds are imposed every year in relation to export bans in distribution agreements or arrangements. Marking invoices "export prohibited" in in breach of EU law, as is withholding supplies for the reason that the supplier does not think the distributor will be supplying his own geographical territory.

2 Letters of intent

A device that is not uncommon in project work or where large production runs are involved is a letter of intent. Where time pressures make it necessary for work to commence before the final details of the contract are negotiated, the seller, or contractor as the case may be, often asks to be protected by a letter of intent. This signifies the intention of the buyer to award the contract to the chosen firm once negotiations are completed, authorises the commencement of work, and, if worded correctly, gives some security for payment of costs incurred by providing that if the contract is not forthcoming the buyer will refund direct expenditure plus an agreed sum in respect of overheads and relieve the seller of any commitments he may have made with sub-contractors. This procedure, although valuable is avoiding delays in commencement, has the following important disadvantages for the buyer:

i   Whereas the wording of the letter does not necessarily constitute a contract, it does almost inevitably in practice tie the buyer to the seller, and the more the work proceeds the more inextricable these ties become. This weakens the negotiating power of the buyer for settling the terms of the contract. For this reason all the really fundamental points, such as price, time clauses, guarantees and limitations of liability should wherever possible be settled before awarding a letter of intent and should be recorded in it. When it is not possible to specify these points beforehand the letter of intent should detail the points to be agreed so that no confusion can occur at a later date about the intentions of the parties. All such outstanding points should be agreed as soon as possible.

ii   The existence of such a letter frequently lessens the incentive for both parties to finalise the contract, and may even mean that the contract is not finalised by the time the work has been completed − a situation which may have serious consequences for the buyer in the event of defects occurring in use of the goods, especially with regard to damage or injury to property or persons.

iii   The seller (as well as the buyer) is free to abandon the project at any time until the terms of the contract have been wholly agreed. Neither party is bound except as to the matters covered specifically in the letter of intent.

iv   Letters of intent are potentially dangerous since the actions of the parties may inadvertently lead to contracts being created either orally or by conduct in excess of the scope of the letter of intent. If it is not to be legally binding write "subject to contract" on it.

A minimum content of a draft letter of intent is shown as Appendix 3 at the end of Part Three.

3 Commercial basis

Standard conditions of contract should form the foundation on which the contract is built. As such they should define the general rights and obligations which experience has shown to be reasonable for the parties to ask for and accept. They should, therefore, be as comprehensive as possible and drafted in such a way that they require the minimum of alteration to meet the widely varying circumstances in any given field of purchasing.

The conditions should be a simple and clear explanation of the rights and obligations under the contract. Attempting to wrap them up in legal jargon is not only a waste of time, it may actually be misleading to the people having to use them. Clarity and simplicity should be the keynotes throughout.

The model standard conditions detailed in Part Three are in no sense 'buyers' conditions. They have been drawn up with the object of being fair and reasonable to both parties so that:

i   they will gain the ready acceptance of both parties, and

ii if they are ever made the subject of litigation they will be upheld by the courts. This latter point is important since, if either the buyer or seller tries to enforce contract conditions which are manifestly unfair they will find little sympathy from the court.

Before any negotiation is entered into it is essential that a checklist is drawn up detailing all the main points of the contract that require a decision. The following items should be included in such a list:

i   Quantity, description and specification of the goods or services required.

ii   Delivery or completion date (see Section 5, page 34 *et seq* 'Sellers default').

iii Delivery point − where do you want to take delivery of the goods and during which hours?

iv   Price − is it fixed or variable? (see Section 4, page 29 *et seq* 'Price-adjustment formulae').

v   Terms of payment (see Section 4, page 28 *et seq* 'Terms of payment').

vi   Whether goods are to be subject to buyer's inspection prior to despatch. Alternatively, are test certificates required?

vii Any special transport or packing requirements.

viii Are any 'free-issue' materials or tooling being provided? (see Section 7, page 41 *et seq* 'Insolvency and bankruptcy').

ix   Are any restrictions on sub-letting necessary?

x   What is required by way of a guarantee − terms, period, availability of spare parts, etc?

xi   Rejection of goods and agreement about arbitration on quality.

xii Conformity with British (BS), International (ISO), European (EN), or other standards.

xiii Undertaking by the seller to provide technical information to enable the buyer's staff to carry out maintenance of equipment.

The above is only a rough guide; there may well be additional points relevant to the buyer's requirements. Nevertheless, the concept of a checklist is an important discipline if problems are to be avoided later.

Always specify in the enquiry or order that it is a condition of the order that the standard conditions are to be accepted. If the seller raises any objections these can then be the basis for negotiation subject to legal guidance. Avoid attempting to amend the seller's conditions to meet one's own requirements.

The above represents the ideal. It is recognised that on occasions, as a matter of commercial expediency, risks will have to be taken and departures made from the practice and principles set out above. Such deviations, however, should be the exception rather than the rule. The interests of the buyer's company will be best served by adopting and adhering to the practices and principles set out in this book as a whole.

4 Terms of payment

Experience has shown that the negotiation of terms of payment has frequently been regarded merely in terms of 'cash' rather than being related to other aspects of the contract, thereby creating problems at a later date when things go wrong.

It is important that the buyer ensures that the invoice is paid in accordance with the terms of the contract. Unwarranted delay in payment leads to many problems for the seller and can result ultimately in more expense for the buyer. Strictly speaking, late payment of valid invoices leaves the buyer in breach of contract. However, unless the contract provides otherwise, delay in payment gives right only to claim for damages for additional costs.

Usually payment terms have a direct relationship to one or more of the following aspects:

- the value of the contract;
- the period over which the contract is to be performed;
- the extent of the contract which is to be performed on site;
- the cost influence to the seller of 'bought-out' items;
- the extent to which a portion of the price should be retained by the buyer (termed retention money) until the end of the warranty period as 'insurance' against the seller not fulfilling his obligations under the contract, eg failure to meet performance standards as defined in the contract.

A contract for the sale of goods is one whereby the seller transfers or agrees to transfer the ownership of (in legal terms 'the property in') the goods to the buyer for a consideration in money called 'the price'. Where the buyer has to concede part-payment of the price before delivery of the goods care must be taken to attempt to safeguard the material value of such payments should the seller find himself in financial difficulties (see paragraph 7.3, page 45).

On the other hand, it might be that the buyer finds himself in financial difficulties and to protect himself the seller wishes to retain some rights over goods which have not been paid for by use of a 'retention of title' provision (see paragraph 7.3, page 45).

Where the goods being supplied contain a very high proportion of some metal the price of which varies widely (for example nickel, copper, tin) a price-adjustment formula might be appropriate (see paragraph 4.3 et seq below).

The points to be considered in contracts of long duration, where a significant element of site work is involved or where 'retention money' might be appropriate are many and varied.

The negotiation of terms of payment will usually be concerned with the options of fixed or adjusted price.

4.1 Fixed price

Some sellers regard fixed-price tendering as an unacceptable commercial risk. Buyers, however, would prefer fixed prices so that their commitments are known before the order is placed. There may be a temptation to pay a premium to obtain a fixed price, but how does the buyer establish what such a premium should be? Remember the buyer is under the same sort of financial pressures as the seller and to concede more than is commercially necessary could endanger the buyer's cash-flow position. It is often impossible to know what has been built into the price or whether the price is even based on costs or is a 'guesstimate' of what the buyer would be prepared to pay to get the goods. This risk can be minimised by the use of competitive tendering.

4.2 Fixed price with stage payments

Here, in effect, the buyer is making an interest-free loan to the seller which may or may not result in a lower price. Where stage payments are agreed they should be related to, and conditional upon, a finite part of the manufacturing programme, eg materials bought, castings machined, etc. It is important to include a suitable clause in the contract to ensure that the goods at each stage of payment become the buyer's property and are, to a degree, protected should the seller find himself in financial difficulties (see paragraph 7.1, page 42).

4.3 Contract price, subject to price adjustment

This method has the advantage that, provided an established method of calculation is used (see paragraph 4.5, below, Contract-price adjustment), the 'gambling' on forward costs is largely removed. It has the disadvantage that the buyer does not know his commitment at the time of order; however, in some cases it is possible to agree a maximum limit of adjustment. The period over which adjustment takes place should only be that up to the agreed delivery date; should the supplier deliver late then he must be held to bear any increase in his costs between the due date and that of the actual delivery.

4.4 Contract price, subject to price adjustment and stage payments

This has the disadvantages of methods 4.2 and 4.3 and, furthermore is more complex, since the buyer is required to pay by instalments an unknown final price. There are two courses of action open to the buyer in this situation:

(i) To adjust the stage payments:

To inflate the tender price as a whole could be said to be unfair to the buyer, since where costs have been met by stage payments it would not be just to allow further inflation on such costs. In order to adjust the stage payments the buyer would need to devise a formula which would take account of any change in the seller's costs at the time of each payment. Payment would then be made by the buyer in respect of the costs, as adjusted by the application of the formula, already incurred by the seller up to the date of each stage payment. However, the derivation of such a formula would be complicated and there is a danger that any potential saving on the part of the buyer could be absorbed by the time spent by him in monitoring and applying the formula.

(ii) To defer adjustment until the final payment:

Here, the buyer would treat the tender price as if it were firm for the period of the contract, the stage payments being apportioned accordingly. On completion of the contract (or the commencement of the warranty period if retention money is involved) the tender price would be adjusted using a nationally recognised formula (eg the BEAMA Contract Price Adjustment procedure)*, for which indices are readily available, the difference between the tender price and the adjusted price being applied to the stage payment due at that time.

———

The British Electrical and Allied Manufactuers' Association (BEAMA) has developed a contract price-adjustment formula which is widely recognised between buyers and sellers in both the electrical and mechanical industries. Various indices for use with the formula, are published monthly by the BEAMA CPA Advisory Service. Other trade associations operate similar systems designed for specific items, eg the Water Tube and Boiler Manufacturers' Association (WTBA) formula for boiler plant and heat exchangers. The BEAMA CPA Contract Price Adjustment formula for use with home contracts, together with a marked example, is illustrated in Appendix 4.

This method is far less complicated than (i) above, and whilst it can be said that the buyer, where the adjustment is a plus figure, is inflating costs for which he has already made payment in stages, this could well be offset by the ease of application of the formula (and the buyer needing to make only one calculation rather than a calculation at each stage payment) and the fact that the buyer has the use of the 'adjustment money' for the period of the contract.

Regardless of which course of action is chosen, where the first payment is some cash with order, this amount should be deducted from the tender price and adjustment only applied to the balance (see paragraph 4.7, below).

4.5 Contract price adjustment

It is not uncommon for sellers to seek to protect themselves by tendering for work on a price-adjustment basis. The principles set out below are common to all considerations or price-adjustment formulae. However, the buyer must appreciate that the negotiation of overseas contracts, where unusual terms of payment or currency matters can occur, makes the subject of such formulae more complex.

4.6 Why have price-adjustment formulae?

Buyers of goods and services would prefer to obtain fixed-price bids, so that they can know their commitment clearly before placing orders. Many sellers of goods and services, however, regard fixed-price tendering as an unacceptable commercial risk when the delivery of goods and services is fairly long term and significant increases in the costs of labour and/or materials can occur between the time of the acceptance of the order and the delivery of the goods or performance of the service.

Taking work on at a fixed price can, in such circumstances, depress the seller's profit margins to such an extent that he finds himself in financial difficulties, and in the ultimate ceases to trade.

The buyer's interest in the seller is that he should provide the goods or services which are ordered, when they are wanted and at a reasonable price. He is not employed to speculate in a particular market and thereby load his price accordingly.

One way to arrive at a reasonable price is to adjust the initial competitive tender in accordance with some nationally recognised indices, such as those published by the Statistical Office in the *Monthly Digest of Statistics,* or figures produced by the relevant trade associations.

Where the seller insists on a price-adjustment formula as a basis for tendering, it will be to the buyer's advantage to invite all others tendering for that particular job to quote on the same basis, providing all quote on a present-day value using a common form of price-adjustment formula. In this way the comparison of tenders becomes much easier than if some are fixed and others are subject to adjustment.

In a seller's market, it might appear that the buyer has no alternative but to accept tenders on the basis of a price-adjustment formula. However, it should be remembered that the adoption of a price-adjustment formula can pre-empt normal market forces, particularly where rapid inflation is coupled with recessions in some trades. Equally there may be a temptation to pay a premium in order to obtain a fixed price, but how does the buyer establish what such a premium should be? (see paragraph 4.1, above).

Where the goods being supplied contain a very high proportion of some metal whose price varies widely (for example, nickel, copper, tin), price-adjustment formulae for these circumstances can be explored and developed with a reasonable and cooperative supplier.

4.7 **What does the buyer want from a price-adjustment formula?**
If the buyer has to accept tenders on the basis of a price-adjustment formula, he wants the following features incorporated:

Fairness to both parties

The formula must be seen to be fair on both sides. The seller should not receive adjustment on the profit element in the price.

It should be remembered that the application of price adjustment is intended to cover only those changes in the seller's costs that he could not reasonably have foreseen at the time of submitting his tender. The formula must accommodate both rises and falls in price levels. The data used to measure the changes must be objective and without local or party bias.

Where the buyer has agreed to pay a part of the contract price at the time of order, the buyer is financing the initial activities of the seller with an interest-free loan. At this point the buyer has received nothing in return for such a payment and his money could well be lost if the seller found himself in financial difficulties (see paragraph 4.4, above). Such part payment should be deducted from the contract price and only the balance be subject to a price-adjustment formula.

Wide acceptance

It is of advantage to both parties to know that the formula is widely accepted. This reduces the extent of argument or negotiation necessary at each purchase, and enables each party to become familiar with the working of the formula. The BEAMA CPA system is one example of such a nationally recognised formula.

Ease of operation

It is of advantage to both parties to have a simple formula which does not involve complex or tedious calculation.

Suitability for the type of work

The formula should fairly represent the type of work being undertaken by the seller for the buyer.

Clarity

There must be a clear statement of the rules to be applied with no room for argument.

4.8 The general form of price-adjustment formulae

Most price-adjustment formulae in common use are very simple and similar to each other.

The general form is:

Adjusted price = (labour element of tender price x labour inflation factor)

+ (material element of tender price x material inflation factor)

+ (fixed element of tender price)

Complications arise from trying to define the basis of the variables in the formulae. The most critical area is of course the inflation factors to be applied. Inflation factors depend on timing and cost trends. Each formula defines a start and finish time for calculating the inflation factor.

For example, materials are normally purchased soon after the order date and delivered well before completion, so it is fair to measure materials inflation over the early part of the contract period, rather than over the whole contract period. Similarly, labour is used principally towards the end of the contract period, and so it is fair to measure inflation of labour costs towards the end of the contract period rather than over the total contract period. Don't forget ... overheads and profit should not be subject to adjustment. In the BEAMA example in Appendix 4, 5% of the contract price is fixed. Buyers are advised not to accept a lower percentage.

4.9 Prices ruling at date of despatch

This should be accepted only where there is no alternative source of supply. The buyer has no way of knowing how the price is arrived at. If the seller has tendered low to get the work he can adjust it later to a more profitable level. Having placed the order on this basis the buyer is obliged to pay whatever the seller demands. If this kind of provision must be accepted, the buyer should endeavour to modify it by providing that changes in the ruling prices should be notified to him before the goods are despatched, and he should then have an opportunity to cancel the order before the actual despatch if the new price is unacceptable. However, the buyer must expect to pay some equitable cancellation charge if he refuses to take delivery of the goods.

4.10 **Prices ruling at date of despatch with stage payments**
Whilst this method may have some advantages for the seller it is unlikely to be acceptable to many buyers. The buyer is being asked to pay by instalments an unknown final price (see paragraph 4.5 above). Obviously if the value of each instalment can be established at the outset the terms cease to be 'price ruling at date of despatch'.

5 Seller's default: remedies for lateness or failure to perform to specification

Damages clauses are those which purport to provide remedies for lateness or failure to perform to specification. Such clauses should not be applied automatically; they should only be used after careful consideration of the effects of such default. Generally, more care should be taken when specifying the completion date of the enquiry and order (see 'Omission', paragraph 5.4 below).

No communication implying action against a seller should be made without first seeking legal guidance.

The following are typical damages situations:

5.1 **'Penalty' clauses**
A penalty is defined as a sum isolated in the contract price in an endeavour to enforce completion, or otherwise to penalise a defaulting party.

Most buyers when they refer to such clauses mean liquidated damages. Clauses in contracts aimed at imposing a penalty on a party failing to carry out their part of the contract are unenforceable in English law. In spite of this some buyers seek to use a penalty device, expressed as a fixed sum payable against lateness in delivery or failure to perform to specification; however, the courts will ignore such penalty statements and treat the case as 'omission' unless they are a true estimate of loss (see 5.2 and 5.4 below).

There is also no truth in the popular opinion that where liquidated damages for delay are applied there shall also be offered bonuses or other incentives for early completion. The two should not be confused; they are entirely independent of each other, ie the contract may provide for liquidated damages alone, for financial incentive for early completion without any provision for damages for lateness, or it may include both liquidated damages and incentive clauses. The decision as to which attitude is adopted must be arrived at by negotiation having regard to all the circumstances of the contract.

5.2 Liquidated damages

This is a legally acceptable method of obtaining reimbursement from a defaulting seller when lateness or failure to perform to specification may have caused the buyer actual loss, without the need for the buyer to have proved loss. Any such loss must have been foreseeable at the time when the contract was formed and the damages levied should be a genuine attempt at pre-estimating the loss. The level of damages set will form the upper limit on the sum of money which can be claimed even though the actual loss may turn out to be much greater. The following is an example of the wording which could, depending on the circumstance, be employed for such a clause:

> 'Should Seller fail to deliver all or any of the Goods by the delivery date specified in the Purchase Order or any extended delivery date agreed under the Purchase Order, Seller shall pay to Buyer x per cent of the contract price for such portion of the goods as cannot by reason of the delay be utilised for the purpose intended for each week's delay or portion thereof up to a maximum of y per cent of the contract price by way of liquidated damages and not as penalty, and the parties acknowledge that such sum is a genuine pre-estimate of Buyer's losses for such delay.'

> **Note:** x per cent and y per cent to be established by the buyer not the seller.

The advantage of this scheme, from the buyer's point of view, is that the money should be forthcoming without recourse to the courts; the seller likes it because it limits his overall liability. However, the clause should make it clear whether the liquidated damages are the total liability of the Seller for such delay or not. If not add "without prejudice to the Buyer's other rights and remedies for such delay". In view of this the buyer should never accept a price-loading for liquidated damages, but should get the tender first, then talk damages. Obviously this type of clause should be used sparingly otherwise if it becomes a standard practice prices will be loaded at the tender stage. Any damages clause may be invalidated by the issue of an amendment to order unless the damages clause is re-negotiated or re-affirmed.

5.3 Time of the essence

Another course open to the buyer when delay could cause significant consequential loss is to make time the prime consideration of the contract. The wording to use in this instance is: 'Time of performance shall be of the essence of this contract'. This converts any delay into an immediate breach of contract and allows the buyer to reject the goods or materials, but this must be done immediately or the concept of 'Time is of the essence' no longer applies. Redress is usually by negotiation, but if the seller is taken to court damages may be substantial, subject only to the buyer's legal obligation to minimise his loss. It is important that, during any negotiation whether orally or in writing, there must be no implication of acceptance of the delay on the part of the buyer.

The buyer should therefore only use the term 'Time is of the essence of the Contract' if it is the buyer's intention to reject late delivery in the event of the stipulated completion date not being met.

5.4 **Omission**

For many orders it is sufficient to omit express mention of damages altogether, and just agree a delivery or completion date, whichever is applicable.

The establishment of such a date, however, is an important factor of the contract which is often not given sufficient attention.

In commercial contracts if the date is perfectly defined, eg 15 March 1993, time will probably be of the essence automatically (nevertheless, where time is especially important it is safer to make express mention as in paragraph 5.3, above). However if the buyer merely stated 'March', '3 months', 'before 31 March' or 'as soon as possible' he would not normally be entitled to any compensation for delay until after a reasonable time had elapsed following the expected completion date. What is a "reasonable time" clearly depends on all the relevant circumstances.

In the latter situations should loss be incurred, redress in the last resort can be obtained via the courts, but the buyer would need to serve notice on the seller requiring performance of his obligations, eg a letter to the effect:

> 'Time of completion under the above Contract (quote order number, date etc.) being past we now require you to complete within 'x' ('x' must be a reasonable time commensurate with the circumstances) of the date of this letter'.

No further remedy would be available until time 'x' had elapsed; it could be several months after the original expected date before a concrete remedy became available. Where damages are awarded in such a case they would be awarded to compensate for loss, subject to the buyer's legal obligations to minimise such loss. The Seller conversely will choose to include wording such as "Although every effort will be made to adhere to any date specified in this Agreement or otherwise for delivery no liability shall be accepted in relation to such delay and time shall not be of the essence." The Buyer should always watch out for clauses which appear to provide for a delivery date but which simply state that the Seller will to try to meet the date.

5.5 Force majeure

If the delivery of the goods by the seller, or the acceptance of the goods by the buyer, is delayed or prevented by circumstances beyond the defaulting party's reasonable control, the circumstances creating the problem are sometime termed *force majeure*. The term has no defined meaning in English law and its use should be avoided unless an express definition is used in the Contract.

Most people know these principles but few feel that they comfortably can answer the question: 'What comprises an event of *force majeure*?'.

Force majeure clauses were initially inserted into contracts to protect the parties against acts of God (flood, fire, tempest, etc.), civil disturbances, acts of war, and government intervention.

There are various ways in which a *force majeure* clause can be drafted and no one form of *force majeure* clause necessarily will be suitable for every contract. However, most *force majeure* clauses contain similar elements, including the principle:

'No party to this contract shall be liable for any failure to perform any one or more of its obligations arising under this contract if and to the extent that such failure is wholly and directly caused by an event of *force majeure*'.

It should be noted that the relief afforded extends only to the failure caused by an event of *force majeure*.

The fact that the failure must be directly and wholly caused by an event of *force majeure* should also be noted. The clause will be of no avail to a contractor who, through his own fault, finds himself in breach of his obligations and casts around for any contribution (however small) from an event of *force majeure* to excuse himself.

An event of *force majeure* is usually defined by establishing a general test:

'For the purposes of this contract, the phrase 'an event of *force majeure*' shall mean any event: (1) the occurrence of which, by the exercise of reasonable diligence, the affected party is unable to prevent or could not have contemplated, (2) the continuation of which, by the exercise of reasonable diligence, is beyond the control of the affected party; and (3) the consequences of which, in relation to the performance of obligations arising under this contract and by the exercise of reasonable diligence, the affected party is unable to prevent'.

It should be noted that this definition requires reasonable diligence to prevent not only the occurrence and continuation of the event but also its consequences on the performance of obligations.

Many clauses then list specific events of varying degress of calamity:

- acts of God;
- compliance with any order or request of any governmental authority;
- acts of war, whether war be declared or not;
- public disorders;
- insurrection, rebellion or sabotage;
- floods, earthquakes, lightning, hail, catastrophic weather conditions or other natural calamities;
- explosions, fires, riots, violent demonstrations or terrorist acts.

It should be noted that there is no reference to strikes or 'nationwide' industrial action. It is now generally accepted that good management of employees is one of the important skills a contractor must have and that the proper exercise of such skills reduces 'local' strikes to events which reasonable diligence will allow a contractor to avoid.

Factors to be considered in a *force majeure* situation are:
A delivery-time extension granted under a *force majeure* situation also extends the period before which liquidated damages (if any) are payable.

'Costs should lie where they fall', ie each party absorbs its own costs associated with the situation.

The seller is not entitled to impose any additional charges in respect of the storage of goods during a *force majeure* situation unless there is provision for such extra charges in the terms of the contract.

Where a price is established relative to a given quantity, no variation in that price basis should be allowed if the buyer is forced to take a reduced quantity owing to a declaration of *force majeure*.

The buyer should pay only an equitable sum in respect of cancellation charges, taking account of the loss that may be incurred by both parties and the degree to which such losses are insurable. The seller should be covered by insurance in respect of consequential losses, eg loss of profits, loss of other contracts, interruption of business etc., and fire or explosion at the seller's works.

Negotiations should therefore be restricted to costs in respect of materials and labour actually expended up to the date of cancellation.

Force majeure clauses are not the panacea for every ill. The clauses generally are designed to establish a safety net to protect the parties to a contract from the consequences of failing to perform obligations for reasons outside the envelope of a reasonable experience. However, it is very difficult to establish a *force majeure* clause acceptable to both parties which defines the envelope. It is likely, therefore, somewhere in such a *force majeure* clause, that a test will be established which depends upon reasonableness. This gives scope for the improper use of a *force majeure* clause to avoid the consequences of a mistake or to squeeze extra payment out of underbid work. This should be resisted firmly; and it is believed the courts of most jurisdictions would support this resistance.

5.6 Performance to specification

Some suppliers offer a single damages clause to cover delay in delivery and/or failure to perform to specification. These are two separate aspects and should be dealt with as such. Losses may be incurred due to late delivery, eg increased labour costs or storage charges for other items of plant. These factors may not necessarily delay completion if the construction programme is reshuffled. However, failure to meet performance to specification at the commissioning stage could incur more significant losses, including consequential losses, eg profits, customer goodwill, etc. This aspect can be dealt with by an additional liquidated damages clause or a prior agreed claims procedure.

6 Financial assessment of the seller

A reduction in viable sources of supply is generally against the buyer's interests since it reduces competition and inevitably leads to higher prices and more difficult negotiations in the long term. The buyer is therefore interested in maintaining the viability of his suppliers.

On the other hand, however, the buyer has to concede commercially as little as possible whilst maintaining his supply of materials, otherwise he himself will become vulnerable to cash-flow problems.

If the buyer is to avoid problems at a later stage it is essential that care is taken in selecting potential suppliers. Observation of the following procedure will help to eliminate the more vulnerable sources:

i   Introduce a progressing expediting system, involving visits to the seller's works.

Use this system to provide information from within the seller's organisation: details of work in hand, adequacy of stock levels, labour relationships and the breadth of the seller's order book. The latter point is particularly important as it indicates whether the seller is dependent on a few large orders.

ii Consult your sales ledger.

If the seller is also a customer of the buyer it will be useful to discover whether he is prompt in settling his account or takes extended credit.

Find out where there has been any change in the seller's attitude as a customer.

iii Assess the seller's financial position from his annual report.

Generally the buyer needs to study several years' reports in order to establish trends and patterns of change. However, there are solvency ratios which can provide a ready indication of the seller's ability to pay his way. Profits may be low or non-existent but the seller can still carry on as long as he can meet his debts as and when they fall due.

(a) The Current Ratio: This is one of the prime ratios of solvency and provides the first indications of adverse liquidity.

$$\text{Current Ratio} = \frac{\text{current assets}}{\text{current liabilities}}$$

Current assets are investments, stock, work in hand, debtors, tax reserves, and cash in hand.

Current liabilities are creditors (including overdraft repayments), taxation, and dividend payments due. As a general rule the ratio should be of the order of 2:1, current assets being twice current liabilities.

(b) The Liquidity Ratio: This measures the ability of the seller to pay his debts.

$$\text{Liquidity Ratio} = \frac{\text{(current assets)} - \text{(stock and work in hand)}}{\text{current liabilities}}$$

The reason for excluding stock and work in hand is that these represent 'locked-up' cash which generally cannot be realised if the seller is being pressed by his creditors. This ratio should be in balance, ie of the order of 1:1.

Failure to meet these ratios does not necessarily mean that the seller is in immediate trouble, although a significant deviation indicates a strong probability.

iv Changes in seller's sales policy:

An indication of how hard profit margins are being squeezed can be gleaned from changes in sales policy. If the seller has traditionally operated lower-than-average prices, offered large discounts, or has had historically a tendency to reduce these prices or to increase discounts to obtain work, he may now be experiencing problems. This will be manifest in an increase in the frequency of price changes, the introduction of price-adjustment clauses or requests for stage payments, a reduction in the advance warning of pending price changes or even a complete move to 'price ruling at date of despatch' or 'date of invoice'. These measures are normal commercial adjustments in times of rapid inflation. However, what the buyer is looking for is the severity of the trend of the change in policy.

7 Insolvency and bankruptcy

For one to contemplate, during the negotiation of a contract, that the other party might become insolvent or bankrupt during the period of that contract would appear to be contrary to the spirit of creating a good business relationship. Unfortunately, however, financial problems, bankruptcy and insolvency have become more prevalent as a result of the ever-changing economic pressures in the world's market places. Indeed, it would be an imprudent man who did not seek to protect himself, as best he was able, regardless of the apparent strength and stability of the party with whom he was negotiating (see Section 6).

Some important aspects requiring consideration in this context are:

i   What is the position of the buyer who has made advance payment of the whole or part of the contract price?

ii If the buyer has paid towards the cost of tooling or provided tooling or free-issue materials, can he recover the tooling or materials to enable production to continue elsewhere?

iii Can the seller recover goods which have not been paid for, in the event of the buyer becoming insolvent or bankrupt?

A contract for the sale of goods is one whereby the seller transfers or agrees to transfer the ownership (of in legal terms 'the property in') the goods to the buyer for a consideration in money called 'the price'. The principle expressed in the Sale of Goods Act is that property passes when the parties intend it to. The Act has more detailed rules than that which should be considered if the parties have not agreed when title passes. More often than not, however, because of the interaction of clauses constituting the contract document, the intention of the parties cannot be clearly established. Clauses which can interact to create uncertainty are, for example, provisions for the passing of property and risk, delivery instructions, terms of payment, rights of inspection prior to delivery, free-issue materials or tooling, retention of title, etc. Where a contract contains most or all such provisions, great care must be exercised in its drafting.

Remember, the time when the ownership of the goods changes hands (the 'property' passes) is absolutely crucial to any remedy one party may have against the other in insolvency or bankruptcy situations.

7.1 Protection for advance payments

Where the buyer has to concede part-payment of the price at agreed stages during the period of the contract, three important aspects must be borne in mind:

i Any payment with order must be defined as a part-payment and not a deposit.

ii Contracts must provide (a) that the goods for which payment or part-payment has been made are identified and the property in them must pass to the buyer as soon as payment is made (b) that the risk remains in the seller, until the goods are delivered to the buyer.
When the buyer has reasonable cause to believe that insolvency or bankruptcy is imminent he should immediately give notice to the seller of his intention to come and take away the goods or materials, the property in which has passed to him, even if work on them has not started or is only partially completed.

In order to provide the buyer with legal rights for the above actions it is recommended that the following special conditions are written into the purchase order:

Special conditions:

i Where Buyer pays part of the agreed total purchase price on formation of the Contract or before any work thereunder is commenced by Seller, and/or where Buyer pays part or parts of the agreed total purchase price at various times or stages during the Contract (whether such payments are made in advance or arrears of given stages in the fulfilment of the Contract by Seller) then such payments are to be regarded as part-payments and not deposits of the agreed total purchase price, and the property in any materials procured for or manufactured by Seller for the purposes of the Contract shall pass to Buyer with effect from the date of such payments up to the total value thereof.

ii If Seller shall suspend or delay the performance of his part of the Contract, Buyer shall be at liberty to give Seller, his liquidator, administrator or adminstrative receiver, manager or assignee, as the case may be, notice by means of telex, fax, registered or recorded delivery letter, requiring the performance of Seller's obligations to be proceeded with, and in case Seller or his liquidator, administrator, administrative receiver, manager or assignee shall not within seven days proceed with such performance to the satisfaction of Buyer, no further sums of money shall be paid by Buyer on account of the contract and in such event it shall be lawful for Buyer to enter upon and take possession of the work wherever situated and to employ any other person to carry out and complete the same to the Contract specification.

Note: The exercise of the power contained in Clause ii above must be carried out as quickly as possible after the seller has suspended or delayed work or deliveries as it would not do to let the liquidator, administrator or administrative receiver disclaim the contract first. Telexes and faxes should be followed by a letter of confirmation.

The buyer's action effectively terminates the contract, but this must not be confused with the situation which arises when time is made the essence of the contract, or the buyer serves notices on the seller requiring compliance with a performance date (see paragraphs 5.3 and 5.4, pages 36-37), as different principles apply to the two situations. It is also necessary to detail, in the purchase order, an amendment to the Passing of Property clauses in the Model Standard Conditions of Contract, Part Three of this book, as below:

Model 1 − Conditions of Contract − Engineering
(Exclusive of Erection):

Delete Clause 5 and replace by:

'The Property (other than that passing under the Special Condition) and the risk in the goods shall remain in Seller until they are delivered at the point specified in the Purchase Order.

Model 2 − Conditions of Contract − Engineering
(Inclusive of Erection or Supervision of Erection):

Delete Clause 7 and replace by:

'The Property in the Equipment (other than that passing under the Special Conditions) shall remain in Seller until it is delivered at the point specified in the Purchase Order'.

Model 3 − Conditions of Contract (for other than Engineering Goods):

Delete Clause 5 and replace by:

'The Property (other than that passing under the Special Condition) and the risk in the goods shall remain in Seller until they are delivered at the point specified in the Purchase Order'.

7.2 Free-issue materials or tooling

Where the contract provides for the buyer to pay the whole or part of the cost of the seller making tooling with a view to the buyer placing orders in due course for goods to be manufactured using such tooling, the problems created by insolvency or bankruptcy on the part of the seller are obvious.

The seller is in possession of the tooling and the liquidator will be obliged to sell it to whoever offers the best price, leaving the buyer only a right to sue for damages for breach of contract — what good will that be with the seller in liquidation? Clearly, it is in the buyer's interest to draft the contract in such a way that, in the event of insolvency or bankruptcy on the part of the seller, the buyer can remove the tooling and continue production elsewhere.

A typical example of such a clause is as follows:

'Where Buyer for the purposes of the Contract pays Seller the whole or part of the cost of the provision of any tooling necessary for the performance of the Contract the property in such tooling shall pass to Buyer when the manufacture of such tooling is complete and it has been satisfactorily tested. Seller shall maintain such tooling in good order and condition subject to fair wear and tear and shall use such tooling solely in connection with the Contract. Seller shall deliver up such tooling to Buyer on demand'.

The effect of such a clause is that after trials the tooling remains in possession of the seller, as bailee on behalf of the buyer. In the event of insolvency or bankruptcy of the seller, the buyer is entitled to require the immediate delivery of the tooling to him. If the seller or liquidator improperly sells the tooling, the buyer will be able to recover the proceeds of the sale.

Protection for tooling lent by the buyer to the seller or for free-issue materials provided by the buyer can be obtained by the use of the following clause:

'Where Buyer for the purposes of the Contract issues materials (including materials, tooling, patterns and the like) free of charge to Seller such materials shall be and remain the property of Buyer. Seller shall maintain all such materials in good order and condition subject, in the case of tooling, patterns and the like, to fair wear and tear. Seller shall use such materials solely in connection with the Contract. Any surplus materials shall be disposed of at Buyer's discretion. Waste of such materials arising from bad workmanship or negligence of Seller shall be made good at Seller's expense. Without prejudice to any other of the rights of the Buyer, Seller shall deliver up such materials whether further processed by Seller or not to Buyer on demand'.

7.3 Retention of title by seller

Retention-of-ownership ('title in the goods') clauses are not, in themselves, new but they were not in general use in British trade until the Romalpa Case in 1976.

Title in the goods is important from the seller's point of view since, if the buyer experiences financial difficulties and cannot pay his debts in full, the buyer's bank will seize all the assets available leaving the seller, as an unsecured creditor, little or nothing in payment of the debt.

The obvious disadvantage for the buyer, faced with a retention-of-ownership situation, is that the value of his assets is reduced to the extent that he has goods in his possession which he does not own and for which he has not paid, and this could affect the willingness of a bank or other lender to provide overdraft or other loan facilities.

However, efforts to retain ownership by the inclusion of a passing-of-property clause in the contract do not necessarily succeed. There have been several cases since Romalpa where judgement has gone either way – each case turned on the particular wording of each clause purporting to retain title in the seller.

One prime element, which arose above all other considerations in the Romalpa case, is that it is crucial expressly to establish a fiduciary (ie holding in trust) relationship between the parties. In such circumstances the retention of title does not need to be registered (as a charge over the buyer's assets) under the Companies Acts. Thus it is no defence to argue that the clause has no effect (is 'void') on the grounds that the seller had failed to register such a 'charge'.

Other important factors which have influenced the judgements are:

i there must be an express duty on the buyer to account for all the proceeds of sale of the goods not just the moneys due to the seller, and

ii there should be a provision for separate storage of the goods by the buyer and for the seller's interest in the goods to be identified.

7.4 Retention of Title in English Law

Although s. 19(1) of the Sale of Goods Act provides that the seller may retain the right of disposal of the goods until certain conditions have been satisfied, and that property in the goods does not pass to the purchaser until those conditions have been fulfilled, it is only comparatively recently that it has become normal commercial practice for sellers to include a clause in their conditions of sale providing that the property in the goods shall not pass to the purchaser until the seller has received payment in full.

For convenience of analysis such clauses may be considered as falling into three categories:

(A) A clause simply providing that the passing of the property in the goods to the purchaser is conditional upon payment to the seller in full of the purchase price.

(B) A clause providing that the property in the goods shall not pass to the purchaser until all payments due from the purchaser to the seller have been made.

(C) clause extending the rights of the seller to the proceeds of sale of the goods and perhaps even to the proceeds of the sale of those goods mixed with others.

Category A

There is no difficulty with this clause provided that the goods remain identifiable and in the possession of the purchaser. Its effect is simply to defer the passing of the property in the goods until such time as payment has been made. The Retention of Title clause does not operate to create a charge in favour of the seller — which would be void against the Liquidator or other creditor of the company unless registered under ss. 395 and 396 of the Companies Act 1985 within 21 days of its being made — because the purchaser never acquires any right in the goods which could be made the subject of a security.

Goods can remain identifiable even if incorporated into others, as when diesel engines were incorporated into generating sets but were identifiable by their serial numbers as being those supplied by the seller and easily disconnected.

However if the goods have ceased to have a separate identity, because they have been mixed with other goods, then the simple clause would be ineffective since the seller would not retain the legal ownership of the goods which is essential if the requirement for registration is to be avoided. One example is where resin was used in the manufacture of chipboard.

While it is possible to draft the clause in such a way as to extend the ownership of the seller to the product resulting from such a mixture, it is difficult to do so in a way which avoids the clause being treated as a charge and therefore void unless registered under the Companies Act. The difficulty is that if the seller were to re-take possession of the product of the mixture of the goods with others and sell the product, then one would normally expect that any excess in the proceeds of sale over the debt due to the seller, should be repaid to the purchaser. But if that is the case then the transfer of the "other goods" in the mixture to the seller must be by way of charge. Then the contract would have to be registered. Registration is not complicated or expensive and for large value contracts could be done to protect the seller. However it must be done for each contract of sale and so is not feasible for the run-of-the mill one-off purchase contract.

Only if the clause provided that the seller was entitled to the whole of the proceeds could that conclusion be avoided but that in turn raises other difficulties — (see paragraph 7.5 below) and even there such a clause is probably created.

There could be a further complication if, say, two sellers were involved and such a clause were to be included in both their contracts. So far this case has not come before the English courts.

For a simple clause such as this described here it is best to add that the buyer must keep the goods separate from other goods, that they will be marked as the goods of the seller and that they will not be resold until payment has been made. A liquidator will usually require a detailed form to be completed before the goods are returned if the buyer goes into liquidation before payment is made. The seller must ensure it can identify not only which are its goods at the premises of the buyer but also which of its goods have not been paid for. Unfortunately if the seller, for example, has sold two electric pumps to the buyer and the buyer has paid for one only but the seller cannot prove which one was paid for, the liquidator is entitled to refuse to allow the clause to operate. This appears to defy logic but is the law. Where possible the seller should put a serial number of the goods on the invoice so such checking can be done. It is also wise to provide that the buyer simply has possession of the goods, are "bailee" of the seller and do not give any rights to the buyer which suggest the buyer is the owner - a right of resale for example can lead to a charge being created - see Category C clauses below. Even for goods which may be used by the buyer in manufacture (mixed goods) it is worth having a retention of title clause, from the seller's perspective, because the buyer will not use all such goods immediately.

Normally Category A clauses are the ones most likely to be legally enforceable and wherever possible clauses of this nature should be included rather than the more complex clauses described below which are much more likely to be held to be void by the courts.

Category B
It used to be thought that by using such a clause no problems would arise at least as long as the goods are identifiable and are in the possession of the purchaser. It is customary to use this clause when the seller is making regular deliveries to the purchaser; its effect is that as long as any sum remains unpaid then title has not passed in respect of any of the goods delivered.

However, recent case law has cast doubt over even a clause such as this, suggesting that it amounts to a charge. The seller must be able to show that payment has not been made for goods which he is claiming back, **not other goods.** Under English law void clauses can be 'severed' (removed) from a contract, and if the rest of the contract can remain in effect then it is valid. It is wise, therefore, with the more complex retention of title clauses to have several sub-paragraphs so that the more dubious provisions can be deleted by a court whilst the rest remain in force. This eliminates the risk of the entire clause being void.

This is an area where case law continuously alters the legal position, so it is sensible to have solicitors examine standard conditions of sale from this perspective on a regular basis.

Category C

In any commercial sale other than to an end-user it is the intention of the seller that the purchaser should use the goods for the conduct of his business either by re-sale of those goods after they have been worked on in some way, or after they have been combined with other goods to produce another product. One or other of these situations must apply, otherwise the purchaser could never carry on his business and earn the money with which to pay the seller.

The purchaser in such cases can pass a good title to a sub-purchaser under s. 25 of the Sale of Goods Act and s. 9 of the Factors Act, provided that the sub-purchaser buys in good faith and without notice of the Retention of Title clause or the fact the seller still owns the goods.

For this reason the seller will often try to extend the Retention of Title clause so that it covers not just the goods themselves but also the proceeds of sale whether those proceeds arise just from the sale of those goods, or whether from those goods mixed with others. Furthermore for his better protection the seller will usually stipulate that the proceeds are to be paid into a separate bank account and held in trust for him. It is here that the difficulties really start.

In order for such a clause to stand a chance of being effective it would appear necessary that the buyer should owe the seller a fiduciary duty in relation to the proceeds of any sub-sale. Such a duty must be expressly set out in the contract. It will not be implied since it is inconsistent with the normal relationship of buyer and seller. Nor will a mere reference to the buyer being a "bailee" be sufficient.

There is again no difficulty in drafting such a clause, although there could be in getting it accepted by a wide-awake purchaser, but the problem would still be of avoiding the requirement to register the agreement as a charge under the Companies Act. The only way appears to be if the clause not only refers to the purchaser as being a bailee and under a fiduciary duty to the seller in respect of the goods and any proceeds of sale, but that this duty includes the obligation to account to the seller for the whole of the proceeds of sale and place them in a separate bank account. Again the commercial acceptability of any such clause must be in doubt although it was essentially the way in which the original Romalpa clause was drafted.

It is also arguable in this latter case that the clause is so much a fiction, which is not intended by the parties to be operated in the way it is way it is drafted, that the Courts should disregard its fictional aspects and treat it for what it truly is, namely the establishment of a preferential charge over the buyer's assets in favour of the seller.

However the general approach of English law seems to be based on a strictly contractual approach to the validity of Retention of Title clauses without taking into consideration the wider policy aspects of the operation of the clause in relation to the claims of other creditors.

7.5 Retention of Title and Passing of Risk

The general rule of English law as stated earlier is that risk passes with property (s. 20(1) of the Sale of Goods Act). If therefore the seller retains title in the goods then, unless the contract provides otherwise, the goods also continue at his risk.

Of course in practice any well drafted Retention of Title clause will provide that, after delivery, the risk passes to the purchaser; the purchaser must insure the goods against accidental loss or damage and hold the proceeds of any insurance claim as trustee for the unpaid seller ie the insurance moneys, in the way as the proceeds of sale, must not be allowed to become part of the purchaser's general assets.

Remember, no retention-of-title provision is valid unless it has been made a part of the contract. Stamping invoices 'goods supplied subject to retention of title' is unlikely to have any effect in law.

The above guidance represents the current state of play in 1992. However, the need for care to be taken and legal advice sought in the drafting of any retention-of-ownership provisions was summed up by Staughton in *Hendy Lennox vs Grahame Puttick Ltd:*

'This area of the law is presently a maze if not a minefield, and one has to proceed with caution for every step of the way'.

8 Product liability

With the accession of the United Kingdom to the Treaty of Rome and full membership of the European Community, fresh impetus was given to the reform of the unsatisfactory nature of UK law pertaining to the liability of producers and suppliers of goods for defective products.

Before 1987, as far as the customer was concerned, product liability was governed by the contract entered into by the buyer and the seller. Damages for a faulty product could be claimed either in 'contract' or 'in tort' (the civil law of negligence). In the absence of some special agreement between the parties to the contrary, the Sale of Goods Act 1979 and the Supply of Goods and Services Act 1982 implied terms into most contracts for sale or supply, that the goods were of merchantable quality and reasonably suitable for the purpose supplied. The Unfair Contract Terms Act 1977 limited the powers of contracting parties to reduce or exclude contractual liability by use of contractual terms, notices or disclaimers.

Except in cases where there was a criminal liability, a person suffering injury from a defective product could only sue the manufacturer or importer in 'tort', and in general terms the person injured was required to prove a manufacturer or supplier negligent before they could successfully sue for damages.

Between 1977 and 1979 four major European reports recommended that the liability of manufacturers for defective products should be tightened, and that the rule to be applied should be strict liability not merely liability for the effects of negligence. The reports were:

- Law Commission Report 1977

- Council of Europe Strasbourg Convention 1977

- Royal Commission on Civil Liability and Compensation for Personal Injury (the Pearson Report) 1978

- EC Draft Product Liability Directive

In July 1985 the Council of the European Communities adopted the EC Product Liability Directive 85/374/EC which aimed at providing the same level of protection, based on the concept of strict liability, for people throughout the European Community. The Directive was given effect in English law in March 1988 by the Consumer Protection Act 1987.

Limits have been placed on the power of the contracting parties to reduce or exclude contractual liability by use of contractual terms, notices or disclaimers, under the provisions of the Unfair Contract Terms Act 1977. The court has the power to declare any exclusion clause in business contracts on standard terms for the sale or supply of goods and services void if it is unreasonable. An exclusion clause seeking to restrict or exclude the seller's liability for personal injury or death caused by negligence is void.

8.1 The Consumer Protection Act 1987

While this Act does not apply to commercial contracts, the Consumer Protection Act 1987 removes the need to prove negligence on the part of the producer, who will be liable whether or not he knew or could have known of the defect. The business purchaser usually has no claim against the manufacturer unless buying direct from him, even when the latter has offered a guarantee and may be better placed to provide repairs or replacements. A retailer, while responsible for the quality of the goods supplied, is, in many cases, in no better position than the consumer to identify the existence of any defects. Where the product is of a type ordinarily intended for private use, and intended by the victim for his private use or consumption, the manufacturer or producer may be liable under the Consumer Protection Act 1987, passed to give effect in UK law to the 1985 EC Directive.

Under the Act an injured person can take action against:

(a) **Producers:** usually the manufacturers, or in the case of raw materials those who mined or otherwise obtained them. Also included are processors (for example pea canners), but those involved solely in packaging are not affected unless the packaging alters the essential characteristics of the product.

(b) **Importers:** meaning importers into the European Community, not just into the United Kingdom. Where goods are imported into another EC country and subsequently sold in the United Kingdom, liability rests with the first importer, not the United Kingdom importer.

(c) **Own-branders:** suppliers who put their own name on the product and give the impression that they are the producers.

Other suppliers, such as wholesalers and retailers, are not liable unless they fail to identify the producer, importer or "own-brander" if asked to do so by a person suffering damage.

Liability under the Act is joint and several; the plaintiff may sue both (or all, if more than two) defendants. It is not possible to exclude liability under the Act by means of any contract term or other provision.

Liability under this part of the Act is not restricted to consumer goods. Unprocessed agricultural products are specifically excluded but all other goods, including those used at a place of work, are included.

Buildings are not covered although individual goods from which they are built (eg bricks and beams) are covered.

Liability under the Act also extends to components and raw materials. If a finished product contains a defect in a particular component, both the manufacturer of the finished product and the component manufacturer may be liable.

The Act is not intended to extend to pure information. Printed matter therefore is not covered, except in the case of instructions or warnings for a product (in which case the producer of the product − not the printer − will be liable for errors or omissions in the instructions or warnings which make the product unsafe). Similarly, a design consultant will not be liable under the Act for a mistake in a design which causes a product to be defective; the producer of the product itself will be liable. Similar considerations are relevant to software. Computer software is often supplied as an intrinsic part of a product and in some cases can cause personal injury (for example airline navigation systems or production-line robots). Again, liability in such cases is imposed on the producer of the product.

Defective products

A defective product is defined in Section 3 of the Act as one where the safety of the product is not such as persons generally are entitled to expect. This definition provides an objective test of 'defective' and refers neither to the particular person not to the particular producer. A product will not be considered defective simply because a safer version is subsequently put on the market.

There are three relevant factors mentioned in the Act which the Court will take into account when deciding whether a product is defective:

− the manner and purposes of the product's marketing; the way it is presented, instructions for use and warnings;

− what might reasonably be expected to be done with it;

− the time when the product was supplied (no inference is to be drawn from the fact alone that more recent products are safer).

The criteria of what reasonably might be expected to be done with a product, and consequently what instructions and warnings are given, is particularly important for producers and importers whose products are often misused.

Damage

A person can sue under the Act for compensation for:

− death or personal injury

− loss or damage to property (including land)

In suing for loss or damage to property, the plaintiff must show that the property is of a description ordinarily intended for private use, occupation or consumption, and is intended by the victim mainly for his own private use. He must also show that loss incurred exceeds £275.

Defences

A producer or supplier can avoid liability if he can prove any of six defences:

- he did not supply the product (eg it was stolen or is a counterfeit copy of his products);

- the state of scientific and technical knowledge at the time he supplied the product was not such that a producer of products of the same description as the product in question might be expected to have discovered the defect if it had existed in his products while they were under his control (the so-called "development risks defence" which was upheld as lawful and in accordance with the Directive from the European Court in 1997);

- the defect was caused by complying with the law. Compliance with a regulation will not necessarily discharge a producer from liability; in order to claim the defence he would have to show that the defect was the inevitable result of compliance;

- the defect was not in the product at the time it was supplied (eg if a product becomes defective because a retailer handles it carelessly);

- the supplier is not in business. This excludes sales of home-made toys to the church bazaar and sales by private individuals of secondhand goods;

- the producer of a component will not be liable if he is able to show that the defect was due either to the design of the finished product, or to defective specifications given to the component manufacturer by the producer of the finished product.

The extent of the defendant's liability could be affected by any contributory negligence on the part of the plaintiff, eg if he contributed to his injuries by his own carelessness.

A plaintiff must begin his court action within three years of being injured by the defective product. An injured person cannot sue under this part of the Act ten years after the defective product was supplied by the producer.

English law imposes restrictions on the ability of the seller to insert into contracts terms which seek to exclude, reduce or limit liability.

The General Product Safety Regulations 1994 (SI 1994/2328) complement the Consumer Protection Act 1987 in this area and implement a later EU Directive - the General Product Safety Directive. They require that only safe products be put on the market in the EU and set out details of what factors are relevant in assessing safety - such as what warnings were put on dangerous products. Anyone breaching the regulations faces a fine.

Normally it is the manufacturer who is liable, though there are lesser offences for mere distributors of products.

There are also, of course, a whole range of sectorally specific pieces of legislation, most based on EU directives, ranging from toy safety to electromagnetic compatibility.

8.2 Liability for defective services

The EC intends now to deal with liability for damage resulting from the provision of defective services, and has submitted to the Council of Ministers proposals for a Directive on the liability of suppliers of services but this proposal has been delayed by many years and in 1997 was still not agreed. The aim is to achieve parity of approach with the Product Liability Directive, by removing the need for an injured party to show that the injury or damage resulted from negligence by the supplier of the services, who will be required to bear the burden of proving the absence of fault. The draft Directive provides that the damage for which a supplier of services will be liable will cover the death or other "direct" damage to the health or physical integrity of persons.

It will also cover direct damage to the physical integrity of movable or immovable property, including animals (presumably classed as movable property), but only so long as the property;

(a) is of a type normally intended for private use or consumption

(b) was intended for or used by the injured person principally for his private use or consumption.

The Directive will also cover any material financial damage resulting directly from the damage just referred to.

The proposal is that the supplier's liability shall expire after 5 years from the date when the particular service was supplied. This period becomes 10 years, however, where the service relates to the design or construction of immovable property. In addition, actions by injured parties must be launched within 3 years from the day when the claimant became aware, or should reasonably have become aware, of the damage, the service and the identity of the supplier. This period too becomes 10 years where the service relates to the design or construction of immovable property.

8.3 Criminal liability

In certain circumstances a manufacturer, supplier or distributor of a faulty product which causes injury to the user can be criminally liable. Such liability usually arises from the infringement of statute or other legislation; two pieces of legislation often cited in such cases are the Health and Safety at Work Act 1974, and the Food Safety Act 1990. Other criminal statutes also apply however, such as the Factories Acts, the Packaging and

Labelling of Dangerous Substances Regulations 1978, the COSHH regulations made under the Health and Safety at Work Act, the Consumer Safety Act and the Trade Descriptions Act. Part II of the Consumer Protection Act 1987 (s. 10(i)) makes it an offence to supply or offer to supply consumer goods which fail to comply with the general safety requirements.

Probably the most far-reaching of these criminal provisions is the Health and Safety at Work Act. Section 6 requires everyone involved in the supply of articles or substances for use at work to ensure their safety so far as is reasonably practicable. The standard of care here is the same as that imposed in civil cases by the common law, as discussed earlier in Section 5, except that there is no criminal liability for injuries caused by misuse of equipment.

Regulations on consumer goods made under the Consumer Safety Act lay down detailed standards of design, construction and instructions to users, breach of which is again a criminal offence. Anyone injured as a result of such breach is entitled to damages. Miscellaneous other important rules concern food and drugs, packaging of dangerous substances, motor vehicle safety etc.

Anyone who supplies unfit or dangerous goods in the course of business may commit a crime also under the Trade Descriptions Act if by word or conduct he has advertised them as safe or suitable for a particular purpose.

9 Buying from abroad

With industry's increasing dependence on supplies from overseas sources, many buyers will be faced with conditions of contract proposed by suppliers which are based on the seller's own law which may differ substantially from English law.

Although it has been recommended that the buyer should always seek to have the contract governed by English law there may be occasions when because of commercial pressures the buyer has to accept the foreign law. Ideally the buyer should only do so after having obtained expert advice on the implications of that law from foreign lawyers; however again lack of time or unwillingness to incur the cost may prevent this. The following therefore gives a brief guide to the most important issues on which the law of most continental countries differs from English law.

Most continental countries are parties to the United Nations Convention on the Uniform Law for International Sales (the Vienna Convention). UK at present has not ratified this Convention. If the contract refers to the law of a country which has ratified the Convention eg Germany or France, then the reference will be taken on an international sale of goods to be to the law of the Vienna

Convention. It is only if the reference states specifically that it is to that country's **domestic law** that the Convention would be excluded. In this latter event then the buyer in his own interests should certainly take advice since the various continental systems differ substantially not only from English law but as between themselves.

As regards the Convention it applies only to sales of goods and not to contracts where the primary obligations are those of providing services, eg a turn-key contract.

The Convention does not cover the validity of the contract, the passing of property or the liability of the seller for death or injury to any person caused by the goods. So issues such as mistake, misrepresentation, or fraud are not covered, nor retention of title. They would be governed by the domestic law of the contract.

In the formation of a contract the Convention departs from English practice in two respects. An offer which is expressed to be binding for a fixed period of time cannot be withdrawn during that period. The doctrine of consideration is not recognised by the Convention. Secondly acceptance of an offer sent by post is effective from the time that it reaches the other party not when it is posted as under the English postal rule.

Modification of a contract is affected by the simple agreement of the parties which for a written contract must also be in writing. Again there is no requirement for consideration.

The rules in the Convention relating to the conformity of the goods with the contract are in their effect broadly similar to those of the Sale of Goods Act. However the buyer must examine the goods immediately and his rights will be lost if he does not give notice of the non-conformity within "a reasonable time" or at the latest two years from delivery, unless the Seller knew or ought to have known of the non-conformity. It is to be noticed that the Buyer loses his rights by not giving notice within due time not, as under the Sale of Goods Act, has his right to reject reduced to a claim for damages.

Two other issues need to be examined. First there is no mention in the Convention of the familiar distinction between "conditions" and "warranties" of the Sale of Goods Act. Instead there is a single provision referred to as "fundamental breach" which gives the Purchaser the right to reject. This is defined as a "breach which results in such detriment to the other party as substantially to deprive him of what he is entitled to expect under the contract, unless the party in breach did not foresee and a reasonable person of the same kind in the same circumstances would not have foreseen, such a result". (Article 25)

This concept overcomes the problem in English law of a buyer being able to reject for breach of a condition when in fact the breach did not deprive him of any real benefit.

Additional to the right to reject for fundamental breach the buyer may also require the delivery of substitute goods and, for defects which do not constitute fundamental breach, he may require the seller to repair the goods unless this would be unreasonable in all the circumstances. The buyer may also, when the goods do not conform with the contract but the breach is not fundamental, make a reduction in the contract price in the proportion which the value of the goods actually delivered had at the time of delivery bears to the value that conforming goods would have had at that time. These remedies derived from the civil law are unknown in English law although of course they may be included in a contract as specific rights of the buyer.

If delivery is delayed then the buyer can only avoid the contract immediately if such delay amounts to a fundamental breach. Otherwise he may give the seller a Notice with a reasonable time within which to deliver and terminate if delivery is not effected within the period of Notice. Even if delivery is made during the extended period for delivery the buyer can still claim damages for the time that delivery was delayed. This latter provision based on German law is useful to the buyer if it is not certain under the contract that failure to delivery by the contractual date would be a fundamental breach.

Finally the Convention differs from English law regarding Frustration and indeed from most clauses which appear in standard forms of contract. It provides that "A party is not liable for a failure to perform any of his obligations if he proves that the failure was due to an impediment beyond his control and he could not reasonably have been expected to have taken the impediment into account at the time of the conclusion of the contract or to have avoided its outcome or consequences".

What is meant by "not liable" is explained in the Convention by stating "Nothing in this Article prevents either party from exercising any right other than to claim damages under this Convention".

By exercising the right therefore the seller can avoid paying damages, but the contract is not avoided and the parties released from their performance obligations, as it would be under English law and under most so-called "Force Majeure" clauses. Thus if for some reason performance becomes impossible now, but could be so in 12 months time and this would still satisfy the buyer, then arguably he could hold the seller to performance of his contract without change of price. Of course if the delay is such as to amount to a fundamental breach the buyer could terminate the contract.

Perhaps rather exceptionally if the seller were unable to deliver conforming goods because of an impediment falling under this Article, then the buyer would have the right of price reduction referred to above, since such reduction is not classified as damages.

The above is only a very brief summary of some of the principal differences between the Convention law and English law. The Convention itself is written in language which mostly is easy to read and mercifully free from legal jargon. Any buyer who may be involved with contracts regulated by the Convention is well advised to familiarise himself with its text.

9.1 UK conditions

Contracts Applicable Law

It is possible simply to adapt the Model Conditions of Contract, contained in Part Three of this book, for use in contracts with overseas suppliers, provided that the following guidance is observed:

i Applicable Law

It is to the buyer's advantage to make a contract under English law since this is the law he knows best. However, the law of another country can be accepted provided legal guidance is sought.

It is of the utmost importance that in all international contracts the law which is to govern that contract should be clearly stated. UK has ratified the Rome Convention 1980 which provides a uniform method for deciding the law governing international contracts, including contracts for the supply of goods and services, to which the Convention relates. The Rome Convention on the law applicable to contractual obligations came into force in the UK through the Contracts (Applicable Law) Act 1990 on 1 April 1991. The Convention is worldwide in effect, providing rules for contracts between member countries in the EC, and applies to all international contracts within the scope of the Convention which would come before the UK courts. The two main provisions of the Convention are, first, that the parties to a contract are free to choose the law that should govern it, with the sole restriction that if all the other elements of the contract at the time of its formation are connected with one country only, then the law of that country must also be applied, and second that, if no election is made, then the contract will be governed by the law of the country with which it is most closely connected.

A suitable model clause covering the issues is:

"This contract shall be subject to English law and the parties agree to submit to exclusive jurisdiction of the English Courts".

ii Arbitration

The use of the International Chamber of Commerce booklet *Rules of Conciliation and Arbitration* is recommended. This gives full details of the system and its application. The word of the arbitrator is final and the party against whom a judgement is made is expected to carry it out promptly. In many countries judgements are enforceable in law.

Do not confuse choice of law and jurisdiction for disputes. Each contract whether disputes are to be settled by an arbitrator or the courts should state which country's laws apply. The arbitrator will need to know this. Separately the contract should state whether disputes will be handled by the courts or instead by arbitration (which is often preferred by those involved in international contracts, particularly where a neutral country can be chosen as the venue for the arbitration".

It may well be possible to retain English law but accept neutral arbitration in which case the following arbitration clause should be used:

"The construction, validity and performance of the contract shall be governed by the laws of England and all disputes arising in connection with the contract shall be finally settled under the Rules of Conciliation and Arbitration of the International Chamber of Commerce by one or more arbitrators appointed in accordance with the Rules. Place of arbitration shall be ......
(Insert a neutral capital city) and language English".

If the buyer is forced to accept a foreign law base he should always use neutral arbitration, amending the wording above to state the law agreed. However, ICC arbitration can be protracted and expensive. It may prove cheaper to accept the ruling of the courts in Western European countries.

iii Passing of property and risk
For deliveries from overseas suppliers always specify the point of delivery as well as the final destination, eg:

Point of delivery	:	FOB Rotterdam
Final destination	:	J Smith Ltd, Empress Works, London.

This is an important aspect of the passing of property and risk.

Many buyers, and sellers, use well known abbreviations like FOB, FAS, CIF, without understanding the full implications of these terms on the obligations of both parties to the contract. Misunderstandings cannot arise if the contract is made subject to *Incoterms 1990*.

Incoterms are internationally agreed definitions of these abbreviations and common trading terms. They define the obligations of both the buyer and the seller for each set of circumstances, and are published by the International Chamber of Commerce, at 14/15 Belgrave Square, London SW1X 8PS.

Incoterms can be introduced into the contract by inserting the following clause:

'Incoterms 1990 shall apply to the Contract provided they are not inconsistent with any of the terms contained therein'.

v **Entry into the United Kingdom**
If the contract requires the seller to send people to do work at the buyer's works, it would assist with customer clearance if the following clause was added to the conditions of contract:

'If tools are being brought or sent to the Site which are to be returned on completion of the Contract a list in triplicate of the tools and their value in Seller's own currency shall be provided not less than 21 days before despatch to facilitate Customs clearance and entry into the United Kingdom. If letters of introduction to facilitate entry into the United Kingdom are required the full names of persons involved shall be provided not less than 14 days before their embarkation'.

9.2 Terms of payment

Obviously there cannot be any prescribed standard in respect of terms of payment since these will have to be negotiated separately for each contract. However, there are certain general aspects which must be borne in mind:

i The problems of combating inflation arising from currency fluctuations need to be carefully considered if one is required to make payment in a foreign currency: dollars, Deutschmarks, etc. Guidance should be sought from someone knowledgeable in foreign exchange matters on the question of forward cover of currency.

ii A fixed price, ie free from price adjustment in respect of labour and materials, is recommended. Price-adjustment formulae based on foreign indices could be more complex (see paragraph 4.5, page 25).

iii Whatever terms are agreed, payment is usually effected by means of a 'documentary credit' such as a bill of exchange or letter of credit.

9.3 Documentary credits

Documentary credits are a secure and very widely used means of payment in international trade.

The term 'documentary credit' is used to define any arrangement whereby a bank (the 'issuing bank'), acting at the request of a customer (the applicant for the credit), is to make payment to, or to the order of, a third party (the beneficiary) against stipulated documents, provided that the terms and conditions of the credit are complied with.

Credits are separate transactions from the contract of sale, although they are based upon the terms of such contracts, and the banks are in no way concerned with or bound by the contract of sale. The banks are concerned only with, and must comply with, the terms of the credit document, therefore the credit instruction must be complete and precise. The use of the International Chamber of Commerce booklet *Uniform Customs and Practice for Documentary Credits* is recommended. This gives full details of the rules and regulations governing documentary credits, and their application.

The banking systems of two different countries are involved with a letter of credit. The credit is raised by the buyer's bank (the issuing bank) and confirmed by a bank in the country of the seller. The confirming bank is not necessarily the seller's own bank but is a bank with which the issuing bank has established a credit relationship (usually termed the 'corresponding' bank).

Credit documents can be drafted such that the credit can be:

i **revocable** − credit may be amended or cancelled at any moment without prior notice to the beneficiary.
For obvious reasons such credits are unlikely to be acceptable to the seller.

ii **irrevocable** − constituting a guarantee by the issuing bank that payment will be made provided that the terms and conditions of the credit are complied with.

iii **irrevocable and confirmed** − as in (ii) except confirming bank guarantees payment irrespective of whether it receives payment from the foreign bank.

iv **transferable or assignable** − this allows the credit to be transferred to a third party (not the seller under the terms of the contract of sale).

v **'back to back'** − a device which is often used where the buyer is 'selling on' the goods to a customer who is also paying by letter of credit. The letter of credit under which the buyer is the beneficiary is used as the credit base for raising the buyer's letter of credit to the seller.

All letters of credit require the 'presentation' of specified documents, evidencing the performance of the contract of sale, to the confirming (corresponding) bank and the acceptance by that bank that the documents are in good order eg not 'stale' (see paragraph 9.4, below) or incomplete, before payment is made. The buyer stipulates what documents he requires from the seller evidencing performance: bills of lading, commercial invoice, certificate of value and origin, test certificate (for materials or machinery) or health certificate (for foodstuffs or pharmaceutical products), etc. The bank has a legal duty to the buyer not to make payment unless the 'presentation' is correct and it is made within the time specified – all credits have a finite life as set down in the credit document.

Assuming the 'presentation' is correct, the credit document will also stipulate when payment is to be made, ie

i **'at sight'** – payment is made immediately the bank is satisfied with the presentation, usually within 48 hours.

ii **'tenor'** – this means the buyer and seller have agreed extended credit terms from date of despatch. Usually expressed as 'payment shall be made 'x' days (eg 60 or 90 days) from the date of the Bill of Lading'.

Banks will reject a letter of credit if there is any defect on the document. It is therefore wise for the seller to include a term in the contract that the buyer will pay all bank charges arising from a letter of credit being rejected.

9.4 Bills of lading

Bills of lading can be likened to transferrable cloakroom tickets. They acknowledge receipt of the goods in a certain condition, and the goods are surrendered to the bearer of the ticket on presentation. In fact, a bill of lading is three things. It is:

i A receipt.

ii The evidence of a contract having been made under internationally agreed rules (called the *Hague Visby Rules*) under the Damaged Goods Act 1971.

iii A document of title.

and potentially it is also a fourth thing, namely:

A negotiable document (ie if marked 'Negotiable').

Unless otherwise specified in the credit, bills of lading must show that the goods are loaded on board a 'named' vessel (marine bill of lading) or 'named' aircraft flight (airway bill).

A 'clean' bill of lading states that goods have been received in apparent good order. If the bill of lading is endorsed to the effect that something is not in order then the terms of the letter of credit may not be honoured by the bank. A 'stale' bill of lading is one presented late by the seller of the goods to the banking system but whether or not a bill is stale depends on the banker's judgement, not on law. It is worth remembering that delays caused by incorrect attention to documentary procedure can be costly (see paragraph 9.3, above).

9.5 Shipping

It is important to define terms such as FOB (free on board); for example 'FOB UK Port' is much too vague — 'FOB Rotterdam' leaves no doubt. As long as both parties have a copy of Incoterms it is generally better just to rely on the definitions of FOB, CIF, etc therein. With regard to the term FIO it must be remembered this is a term written from a shipowner's point of view, ie Free In and Out to the shipowner, which means the shipper pays for loading and discharge. In the case of CIF (cost, insurance and freight) it is worth bearing in mind that the goods belong to the buyer when put aboard the vessel at the port of despatch.

When considering whether to buy FOB (or Ex Works) rather than CIF or delivered, it is useful to check the cost of carriage — it is not uncommon to find the difference between FOB and CIF prices represents a fictitiously low rate of freight thus indicating an unwillingness to quote openly a realistic FOB for reasons best known to the seller. Obviously a CIF purchase is best in these circumstances.

When ships are chartered, there are essentially three different types of charter that can be presented to the buyer:

i   Bare-boat charter: This is rather like hiring a self-drive car. The charterer is responsible for everything including crew, fuel, victualling, dues, etc.

ii Time charter: This is rather like hiring a chauffeur-driven car. The charterer pays an agreed amount per day but also pays for fuel and dues.

iii Voyage charter: This is rather like hiring a taxi with the fare agreed before the journey begins.

Chartering arrangements are usually made through a chartering broker. Shipowners willingly pay a commission to the broker as this is how they pay for a sales force which could not be economically deployed worldwide if run as part of the shipowner's organisation. A broker's code of practice prevents him keeping rates high to gain extra commission and furthermore he knows he will not continue to get business from charterers if he adopts such a practice.

In making chartering arrangements it is wise to remember there is more to consider than the level of freight rate although this is a prime factor. Lay days between which a shipowner is deemed to fulfil his contract have to be selected and agreed, terms for demurrage have to be settled, and if those are onerous an attractive freight rate can in the event turn out to be much more costly than expected.

The opposite to demurrage is despatch money which means the shipowner gives a rebate for quick loading provided terms for this are agreed beforehand, otherwise the charterer does not benefit. Notice of readiness is usually six hours from the time the ship is presented in a fit state to load but agreed loading/discharge time starts to count if charterer elects to load/discharge at a time within the notice of readiness period. Adequate agreed time for loading and discharge needs to be fixed and whether or not Saturdays, Sundays, and holidays are workable − the quoted freight rate depends on all these factors.

When a voyage charter is arranged for any agreed tonnage then dead freight is payable on any tonnage short-shipped, inflating the cost of the freight on the actual quantity loaded.

10 Negotiation of hire/service agreements

There has been growing tendency towards hire or lease rather than to commit capital to finance plant replacement or expansion. There has also been a growth in the number of companies that provide maintenance services, since many companies have discovered that an outside contractor can often provide this service adequately at a lower cost than by using their own resources.

The purpose of this section is to highlight the important aspects which need careful consideration when contemplating leasing and hiring, other than in respect of land or buildings which are very specialised areas needing expert guidance in each case, or when negotiating a service agreement.

10.1 Financial considerations

i Leasing: this is a complex subject. It is a purely financial agreement, usually arranged through a finance company, and it does not normally concern itself with either the initial selection or the subsequent maintenance of the equipment throughout its working life. In effect it is a money-lending operation and as such experienced guidance should be sought.

ii Hiring: usually effected directly with a manufacturer or distributor and bringing other benefits such as improved maintenance and service arrangements, guaranteed cover, eg hire of a transport fleet, fork-lift trucks, etc.

Consequently, the degree and duration of the commitment by the user is greater in leasing than it is in hiring.

iii Service: can take the form of scheduled maintenance or the performance of a long-term service function, eg security services, office cleaning, etc.

Maintenance agreements are usually effected directly with the manufacturer or distributor as a separate transaction and can be applied regardless of whether the equipment concerned is leased or purchased. Hiring usually includes maintenance.

iv Comparison of alternatives: in comparing outright purchase with the alternatives it is important to be sure of comparing like with like and to make, where necessary, due allowance for a particular advantage attaching to the one alternative which might not be available in the other case, examples being a favourable maintenance contract or the opportunity to contract out of obsolescence or to obtain a capital gain.

Then in comparing the straight financial alternatives, it is necessary to recognise that most leasing arrangements still leave many of the risks associated with ownership with the user without the advantages of ownership and that a leasing arrangement is similar to that of purchasing the asset and taking a loan in all but the balance sheet presentation.

In current circumstances, the considerations affecting the choice of the method of finance are, therefore, reduced to the question of whether, after taking taxation and associated incentives into account, the finance could be provided from one source more cheaply than from another.

Experience has also shown that, where manufacturing plant is leased, practical difficulties can arise if it is desired to improve or modify the plant. It is necessary to obtain the prior written consent of the lessor, which can cause delays, and any additions to plant will usually have to become the property of the lessor who is under no obligation to advance the money to pay for them.

10.2 Period of hire

This aspect needs very careful consideration otherwise the hirer may find himself committed for a longer period than is necessary as many of those hiring photocopiers and mobile telephones have found to their cost.

Is the commitment for a finite period, or for an initial or minimum term and thereafter indefinite as to the completion date, or totally indefinite as to the completion date? The term 'evergreen' is commonly used to describe commitments where the completion date is not defined.

If subject to a minimum period, are any liabilities incurred for termination before the expiry of such period? Where such liabilities exist are they commercially acceptable?

How firm is the requirement for the equipment?

Examples of clauses imposed by the other party in this respect are:

i 'If this Agreement shall be terminated at any time before the expiry of the minimum period of hire the Hirer shall be liable to pay to the Company in addition to any rental or other moneys due and unpaid at the date of such termination a sum equal to the total of the rentals which would have become payable for the balance of the said minimum period as liquidated or agreed damages.'

ii '... may terminate this contract by notice in writing to the Hirer and thereupon (if the fixed period has not expired) the Hirer shall pay to the Company a sum equal to rent at the rate payable at the date of the notice of termination for a period equal to the balance of the fixed period unexpired less an allowance of 25 per cent of the said sum in respect of the re-use value of the Equipment and the estimated cost of maintenance thereof during that period.'

iii 'If this Agreement is terminated before the expiry of the minimum period the Hirer shall pay to the Company by way of liquidated damages a sum equivalent to one-twelfth of the annual charge for each month or part thereof by which the minimum period is shortened as a result of such termination but without prejudice to any of the Company's subsisting rights under this Agreement. The Company shall not be obliged to make a refund of any charges paid in advance in respect of any period subsequent to the minimum period.'

The hirer must decide, having regard to all the circumstances, what form of provision in this respect would be acceptable to him.

10.3 Terms of payment
These are usually expressed as either monthly, quarterly or yearly in advance. Where payment quarterly or yearly in advance is agreed there should also be a provision for reimbursement in respect of any unexpired period for which payment has been made in the event of termination of the agreement otherwise than through default or breach of contract by the hirer.

10.4 Variation of charges
The circumstances in which the hire rates can be varied, together with any limitation to such variations or their frequency, must be clearly stated. The hirer must have the right to terminate the agreement, without liability, if any proposed variation is unacceptable. If the charges are subject to an escalation formula, the formula and the cost indices to be employed must be clearly defined and must be easily accessible to both parties (see Section 4, page 22 et seq).

10.5 Rights of termination
These must be carefully checked for the rights and obligations of both parties. Care should be taken with regard to the interrelationship of the clauses containing termination rights and particular attention paid to the effects of termination due to:

i Default by either party

ii Unacceptable price-change proposals

iii Loss of, or damage to, the equipment

iv Cessation of the requirement for the equipment.

With regard to the last point, a further aspect to watch is the period of notice of termination that has to be given in order to prevent automatic extension of the period of the agreement.

10.6 Types of service contract

It is obviously essential to make it clear what services are required. A number of different arrangements can be considered, as follows:

i A contract for a specific task, eg to carry out a specific overhaul programme or undertake a specific duty, such as security service.

ii A contract for preventive maintenance − this includes carrying out regular preventive maintenance routines.

It can be negotiated to include or exclude spares and materials.

iii A contract for preventive maintenance, plus an emergency corrective service. This is the same as (ii) above, with the addition of arrangements for emergency services inclusive in the agreement.

iv A contract for preventive maintenance, plus an 'at-cost' emergency service. Costs for the emergency service are calculated as they arise and are not included in the charges for preventive maintenance.

v Emergency 'on-call' service only − this type of contract is self-explanatory.

vi Professional services, implied service and maintenance contracts. It should be noted that the responsibilities for provision of services is 'only to use reasonable skill and care'. This is in contrast to requirements of Sale of Goods. The user should consider using Express Terms.

Because of the wide variety of equipment and varying requirements for maintenance, it is sometimes not practicable to produce a 'standard' form of agreement. No matter which type of agreement is selected, it is essential to devise effective procedures to monitor the performance of the contractor. Information regarding the occurrence of work and the time taken, as well as details of what work was carried out and what parts and materials were used, should be recorded. The work must be inspected by an authorised person to ensure that the work has been carried out satisfactorily.

10.7 Standard of service

This can be extremely important depending on the type of equipment concerned. Seven days' notice of the need for service may be perfectly acceptable for some equipment, however, a 2-hour call-out might be needed for equipment essential to day-to-day operations. Make sure there is also a time specified for fixing a defect.

Where is the nearest service depot? Can service be obtained outside normal working hours when essential — if so at what charge? Does the agreement cover both preventive and corrective maintenance or merely the latter?

Are replacement parts chargeable?

Where preventive maintenance is to be provided it is advisable to agree and record in detail what this actually means in terms of the equipment and the frequency of visits and provide the contractor with the names of personnel authorised to request service, limiting the number of such personnel.

10.8 Liability for loss or damage

It is fairly common practice for the contractor to seek to exclude all his liability for loss or damage howsoever arising. Obviously the employer will have to accept liability in respect of damage or injury arising from misuse. (Here 'employer' is used as the person using a contractor, not an employer in the legal sense). However, care should be taken not to relieve the contractor of his liabilities for loss or damage to the equipment or surrounding property or for injury to persons where the same arises from negligence or any act or omission of the contractor, his servants or agents. Whilst any such clause would be subject to the provisions of the Unfair Contract Terms Act 1977 (see Section 1) the inclusion of the following indemnity clause, or wording having similar effect, is preferred:

'The Contractor shall take every practicable precaution not to damage or injure any property or persons. The Contractor shall satisfy all claims founded on any such damage or injury which arise out of or in consequence of any operations under this Agreement whether such claims are made by the Employer or by a third party against the Contractor or against the Employer, and the Contractor shall indemnify the Employer against all actions, demands, damages, costs, charges and expenses arising in connection therewith, provided however, that nothing in this condition shall render the Contractor liable for any injury or damage resulting from any negligent act or omission of the Employer, his servants or agents'.

In practicable terms the risks associated with the equipment must be evaluated; the above clause would be a bit heavy-handed for, say, the hire of a typewriter.

Where the service agreement is in respect of equipment owned by the employer, it is also worth while including the following clause to prevent the service agreement continuing should the equipment be destroyed, eg by a fire:

'In the event that the Equipment is destroyed or otherwise so damaged as to be incapable of economic repair then the Employer may terminate this agreement forthwith by notice in writing to the Contractor. The Employer shall pay the Contractor all charges due and unpaid under the Agreement up to the time of such termination provided that the Employer shall not be liable to make payment in respect of any period following the date of termination.'

The above clause must not be used without the preceding indemnity clause, or equal provision, since on its own it could limit the employer's right of action should the loss be the fault of the contractor.

The following are examples of clauses which are unlikely to be acceptable:

i 'The Contractor shall at all times use his reasonable endeavours to maintain the equipment in good working order and supply all component spares necessary for that purpose. However, the Contractor shall not be liable for any financial loss, either actual or potential, suffered by the Employer resulting from any malfunction or unserviceability of the Equipment.'

ii 'The Contractor shall provide all necessary tools and test equipment, together with all component spares required to ensure the operational efficiency of the Equipment. The Employer shall be responsible for the provision of all operating materials such as ribbons, paper tape and paper rolls and shall meet the cost of rectifying damage to the Equipment caused by other than fair wear and tear.'

iii 'The Employer shall arrange all necessary insurance covering the loss of and/or damage to the Equipment. The Contractor shall accept no responsibility for any accidents to persons (other than the Contractor's authorised staff,) and/or property arising from the operation of the Equipment or from the supply of power thereto and the Employer shall indemnify the Contractor against all claims arising out of the foregoing.'

iv 'Neither the Company nor its servants or agents shall be liable for any loss or damage arising or resulting from:

a) any defect in or failure of the equipment howsoever caused

b) any delay in carrying out its obligations under this agreement howsoever caused

c) any act, negligence or default (whether wilful neglect or otherwise) of the Company, its servants or agents, in the manufacture, installation, inspection, maintenance, repair, extension, modification, transfer or removal of the equipment or otherwise howsoever.'

10.9 Assignment

The contractor should not be permitted to assign the agreement or sub-let any part of the work without the other party's written consent.

10.10 Maintenance charges

The charges to be paid must be clearly stated in the agreement, and if the agreement provides for both preventive and corrective maintenance separate provisions are usually required for each aspect.

The following are typical of such provisions:

i Regular Service Hours are 0830 to 1700 hours Monday to Friday inclusive (but excluding Bank Holidays).

ii Preventive maintenance
The Contractor shall keep the Equipment in good working order by providing scheduled Preventive Maintenance during the Regular Service Hours for 'x' days each month/quarter/year (example only – delete as required), taking all necessary steps to keep the Equipment in use, so far as is reasonably possible.

Charge: £0.00 per month/quarter/year.
(example only – delete as required)

Invoices shall be rendered after each visit.

iii Corrective maintenance
The Contractor shall provide unscheduled on-call Corrective Maintenance, as requested by the Employer, to repair faults in the Equipment.

Charge: £0.00 per hour whilst working on the Equipment, plus £0.00 fixed charge per Engineer per visit to the Employer's premises.

Invoices shall be rendered after each visit and must be accompanied by timesheets in respect of each visit which have been duly certified by the person authorising the request for maintenance.

iv The maintenance charges under (ii) and (iii) above include for the replacement by the Contractor of worn or otherwise defective parts on an exchange basis.

The circumstances in which the charges can be varied, together with any limitation to such variations or their frequency, must be clearly stated (see paragraph 10.4, above). Be wary of the imposition of 'travelling time' charges which can often be charged to more than one 'Employer' for the same journey to nearby premises.

11 Negotiation planning

Throughout this book, references are made to "'negotiation'". This facet of purchasing and contracting warrants detailed guidance notes, but, in addition buyers should undergo specific training in the required techniques before engaging in any discussions with potential vendors or contractors. Remember, the opposition are likely to be trained and experienced campaigners, and any indiscipline on the part of the buyers will be pounced upon and translated into reduced risk for the seller, to the buyer's disadvantage.

11.1 Preparation and planning the approach
Under this heading several aspects should be considered. However, in most cases, the first point will be **the objectives − or what is the purpose of the negotiation?** − all concerned should know this.

11.2 Agenda
This is the one of the most important items in pre-negotiation preparation and frequently one of the most neglected.

   i **Always have a list of all the points** to be discussed in a logical sequence. Certain points may need to be discussed in a set order so that one knows whether or not concessions can be made on certain other points.

   ii **Always try to settle technical aspects first.** Until the specification has been agreed there is normally little point in embarking upon commercial negotiations, because if the specification is not cleared there probably will not be agreement.

   iii **Ensure that all points are covered** as this will save considerable time later and possibly avoid misunderstanding that can occur with the consequent loss of goodwill. This is particularly important when dealing with overseas companies whose representatives may not be fluent in English.

   iv **Ensure that the other party has a copy of the agenda** − even if it is an edited version − so that they come properly prepared and bring the right people.

11.3 Selection of team, leader, and location

   i **Composition of team**

     (a) **Make sure that there is a representative to cover each aspect** to be discussed. This does not mean that there has to be a separate person for every major point because some members of the team should be able to cover several points.

(b) **Find out about the other party's team** and ensure that the skills they have available are adequately represented in your own team and that they are bringing the correct people.

(c) **Avoid any unstable or garrulous characters.** The team must be a team and not a collection of individuals.

(d) **Keep the team small** and limit the numbers to the people who are absolutely essential. If negotiating 'at home' others can be on stand-by to be called if required − and they should leave when they have made their contribution. The more people there are present the longer it is likely to take to complete the negotiation.

(e) Remember you do not have to match the other party in numbers.

(f) Finally are there any 'specialists' such as lawyers or interpreters required?

ii **Leader**

(a) The leader tends to be either the senior manager present or the person with the greatest knowledge about the item which is the subject of the negotiation.

(b) **However, it may be better to have an alternative** person as leader, thereby easing the burden on those who have to make decisions or who have some other major contribution to make.

(c) **Always ensure that both parties to the negotiation know who the leader is,** and make quite sure that there is only one leader.

(d) **It should be the leader who eventually agrees** that the agreement will be made having consulted others involved. Other members of the team must take care not to commit the company in advance.

(e) **The leader should ensure that there is only one meeting** going on and should keep the discussion under control.

iii **Location**

(a) There are three main possibilities − 'home', 'away' or 'neutral'.

(b) Consider going to the location where the item concerned is to be built or designed or can actually be seen, if this will assist in the negotiations.

(c) If the choice of location does not readily resolve itself the choice should be that of the client.

(d) Neutral ground such as a hotel room is a possible alternative location. This is particularly useful if the project is secret or if considerable distance separates the two parties and to meet halfway would be convenient for them both.

11.4 Assessment of the 'opposition'

i **Make sure you know their leader** and accord to him the respect due to his position.

ii **Remember to acknowledge the skill or experience** of each member of the other party − even if you don't agree! Also, ensure that you know what areas or activities they are representing at the negotiating table.

iii **Treat any junior member of the other party's team with the same courtesy** that you accord to the seniors. It pays to remember that we were once in junior positions and also that junior people frequently arise to very senior positions − at times with remarkable speed!

iv **Ensure that the other party has the necessary people to cover the points to be discussed** at the appropriate level. Find out in advance the names of the members of the other party and see if you can learn anything relevant about the individuals concerned. Obviously one should also be fully briefed about their company and, if it is an overseas organisation, their country.

11.5 Briefing and rehearsal

For certain major or important negotiations it may be useful or necessary to have a briefing session before meeting the other party. It may be appropriate to remind your team of the following points:

i **Assessment of negotiating strengths and weaknesses**
The situation here depends very much on whether you are negotiating as a buyer or a seller. As a buyer the position might be influenced by factors such as:

(a) **Buyer's or seller's market**

(b) **Competitive situation** − are there several possible suppliers or only a few, or even a monopoly situation?

(c) **Budget situation** − is the budget tight or too low?

(d) **Delivery situation** − is a short delivery required, thereby restricting the number of possible suppliers?

(e) **Are there options on quality,** or service, or guarantee? As a seller the position might be influenced by factors such as:

The requirement to obtain the order owing to surplus capacity or the need to retain the lead in a particular field

Importance of the client to your business

Profitability of the business − or at least contribution to overheads

Future business that is likely to follow

Breaking into a new field.

The next point to remind your team is:

ii **Limits of authority**
If there are limits on the authority of the people negotiating − and there frequently are − then these should be clearly understood before negotiation. It may be useful or essential to ensure that a higher authority is available, even if only at the end of a telephone, for any further approval or guidance that may be necessary.

iii **Security**

(a) If you have to make reference back by telephone or telex, security is a vital consideration

(b) Do not leave documents lying around

(c) If confidential data is being divulged it is essential to sign a secrecy agreement first.

iv **Rehearsal**
After the briefing it may be worth while to 'rehearse' parts of the negotiations and have one or two suitable and senior members of your company taking the role of the opposition. It nothing else, a rehearsal should enable all concerned to decide exactly what is wanted and the minimum period of time acceptable.

Part Two:
Contract Strategy Planning, Award and Administration of Contracts

12 Pre-tender stage

12.1 Project organisation

Contracting is a risk occupation. A company usually chooses to contract out some or all of the work because it does not have the resources or expertise to carry out the work itself. By contracting out however the company is endangering its investment. It has to rely on the competence and continued interest of a contractor. Equally the contractor is risking his profit and indeed his future existence on his ability to interpret accurately the client's requirements. Consequently both partners set out to minimise their own areas of risk.

If a client organisation does not plan, does not use its resources properly, does not move with market trends, does not recognise the present worth of its own money, and overall ignores the commercial aspects of contracting, then the investment is at greater risk with additional knock-on effects on the contractor.

The project organisation is established therefore to formulate and execute the client's plan. The size and interests of the team will be influenced by the strategy adopted for the project. For example if a managing contractor is to be used, then a smaller project team may be justified compared with the situation where the client intends to manage all contracts with his own staff.

Key members should be appointed as early as possible and should be expected to stay for the duration of the project. The key members are likely to be responsible for:

Project managing

general engineering

operations

quality assurance

contracts, materials, cost control and planning.

The overall team must be flexible and is likely to change during different phases of design, building and commissioning.

Each team member should possess a well defined job description to describe his extent of involvement, and level of authority.

12.2 Planning

12.2.1. Development of a project and contract plan

The extent of planning carried out by an organisation will usually depend on the size of the company, the complexity of its projects and the expertise and resources available. One point is certain, however: if no planning is carried out then the company puts itself at risk and the participating contractors and suppliers as well. This results in additional costs and loss of time.

The contract plan cannot be developed until the initial project plan has been produced.

The key points to be borne in mind when devising the project plan are:

The plans should be simple to ensure compatibility within the company, contractors and suppliers.

They should contain contingency plans for each area of risk.

All interested parties should have an input into the information of the project team and the setting of objectives and constraints.

The extent of use of computer systems must be established.

Major organisations indulge in extremely detailed project-planning systems that enable continuous progress monitoring to be established. This degree of network planning cannot be expected in a small company but, whatever level of project planning is favoured, it is always necessary to ascertain the size and content of the project team, together with the controls required relating to programme, cost, quality and changes before the contract plan can be considered. It is during the project planning that the conflicting constraints of high quality, low cost and short time will be evaluated and when this analysis has been completed the contract plan can take shape, ie

How many contracts will be required?

What forms of contract (lump sum, measured, or reimbursable)?

How much time is available for tendering and evaluation?

Should a managing contractor be appointed?

What will be the composition of the documents for each contract?

Will the advantages of competitive tendering be available?

12.2.2 **Forms of contract**
The contract plan will include the decision regarding the form of contract to be adopted. Basically there are three forms − lump sum, measured, and reimbursable, although there can be variations adapted for each type. Let us look at each type and analyse the advantages and disadvantages.

It must be understood, however, that the forms are associated with the allocation of risk to either the company or the contractor and the following analysis demonstrates that whilst the contractor assumes all, or nearly all, the risk in a lump sum contract the spectrum changes through the measured form until the risk is entirely with the company in a reimbursable form of contract.

(a) **Lump sum form of contract**
In this form the contractor quotes a sum for carrying out a specified amount of work by a specified date. The sum may be fixed or subject to adjustment for fluctuations in the cost of labour and materials (see Section 4, page 22 et seq.).

In order to quote a lump sum the contractor is entitled to expect that the specified design is 100 per cent complete, or at the very least 80 per cent complete. Market conditions should also be stable with an absence of major political or economic uncertainties, ie there should be a reasonable financial risk to the contractor.

Consequently, the company must supply to the contractor sufficient information to enable him to establish the following during the tendering period:

specification of work including material supply

technical standards

man-hours and labour disciplines required

types of plant

site organisation

free-issue materials lists

programme key dates

commercial and contractual clauses

It will be evident therefore, that unless the project and contract planning enables the above details to be made available to the contractor then the lump sum form of contract will be the wrong form for that particular contract.

Advantages

- Cost control is safeguarded by the knowledge of the contract cost at the outset.

- The contractor takes the greatest risk allocation.

- The contractor has the motivation due to his commitment on time and cost.

- Usually the competitive elements in this form attract a lower tender price.

- In view of the extent to which performance influences profit, the contractor will tend to use higher-quality staff.

- The company needs only to monitor the progress of the work, thus saving considerable manpower costs.

- Terms of payment can be related to specific milestones of completed work.

Disadvantages

- As the contractor has taken the commercial and contractual risk in his price, the company's ability to influence the performance of the work is minimal.

- There must be close control of change. Whilst the company must retain the right to vary the work, each variation puts the contractor at risk, thereby the company is affected.

- The company has a mixed role. The contractor controls the work but the monitoring activity of the compny must be supplemented by close quality control to ensure that a lower quality is not incorporated to maximise profits or shorten programme times.

- Procedures must be adopted to ensure that the cost and time implications of proposed variations to the work are analysed in relation to the overall effect on other project aspects before the contractor is authorised to proceed on the variation.

(b) **Measured forms of contract**
If the company is unable to specify the full extent of work to be carried out, the contractor can be asked to submit a series of rates associated with units of anticipated work. Payment is made on a measured basis using the tendered rates and the actual quantities or measurements involved. The rates are in fact small lump sums and should all be self-sufficient irrespective of the quantities eventually utilised.

Bills of Quantities are commonly used in civil engineering contracts, each bill representing a trade: concreter, painter, etc. The contractor again quotes rates against estimated quantities and usually quantity surveyors will assess the value of work carried out monthly in agreement with the contractor, and payment is made accordingly.

The following information must be available for the contractor:

sufficient definition to provide an approximation of the scope of work

free-issue materials lists

inclusion of all significant work items in schedule form for pricing. (Post-contract negotiation of additional rates is always harder.)

Advantages

− The contract can be awarded in advance of final design thus allowing earlier progress of the work.

− Change control is minimal because the measurement against work done will cater for the majority of variations.

− The contractor has an incentive to control the performance of the work because his profit is limited by his pricing strategy in the rates.

Disadvantages

− The company assumes the risk of cost control and time.

− The cost of engaging quantity surveyors is borne by the company both directly and indirectly.

− The contractor may have priced his rates to enable him

to over-recover his costs during the earlier stages of the contract at the expense of under-recovery at the end. Consequently an Incidence-of-Expenditure Curve must be drawn at the tender evaluation stage to ascertain the possible recovery from the rates, in relation to progress. This evaluation is required for both competitive tendering and single-tender action.

- If the pricing of rates in this way is allowed to remain, then there will be no incentive for the contractor to perform towards the completion of the work.

(c) **Reimbursable forms of contract**
As the title implies, the contractor is reimbursed for all his costs. He carries out work to the instructions of the company and he is paid against time sheets submitted that detail all hours or days expended by each staff, priced at tendered rates. Materials would be supplied at cost plus an on-cost. Sometimes the profit element and certain overheads are removed from the time rates and form a 'fee' which is paid at interim stages of the contract thus acting in a small way as an incentive for the contractor to perform. This form is usually called a 'cost plus fixed fee' contract and is one of many types of reimbursement. Target cost forms are often negotiated as an attempt to agree a pre-determined target cost and subsequently sharing savings or extra costs compared with the target. The programmed completion date is also a target and attracts a similar sharing of costs associated with over-runs or early completion.

Advantages

- The company is able to contract at a very early stage of the project thus allowing the use of the contractor's resources for design, or procurement of long-lead items.

- It is usual to restrict the tendering to the firm or firms that have operated successfully with the company on a reimbursable basis in the past.

- The company can have complete control of the work.

Disadvantages

- The contractor's risk is limited to the composition of his daily rates and the risk of not getting future work if he fails to perform.

- The eventual cost of the contract is not known.

- The incentive is for the contractor to keep the contract operating for as long as possible because he is in a no-loss situation.

- It is difficult for the company to audit actual man-hour expenditure.

- The company's manpower commitment is the greatest, having taken all risks relating to time, cost and quality.

(d) **Turnkey form of contract**

This is a strategy whereby a company can elect to place the whole project in the hands of one contractor instead of awarding several contracts to specialists and controlling the interfaces either itself or by engaging a managing contractor. The turnkey contractor would expect to carry out the conceptual design, detailed design, and the complete construction, and be responsible for the total package. In theory the company would be expected to allow the contractor to proceed unhindered through to completion but it is unlikely in practice. A company will require to be appraised of progress and will certainly demand an involvement in checking quality. The contract price is usually a lump sum with intricate terms of payment that reflect milestone incentives and payments to sub-contractors.

12.3 Tender documentation

12.3.1 The tender list

In some countries and certain organisations tenders are received as a result of 'open tendering', ie the client advertises for tenders to be submitted for work to be carried out as detailed in enquiry documents that can be obtained from the client. An advantage of this system is that tenderers will apply only if they are interested and have the capacity and resources available.

The compilation of a tender list however is a critical operation, especially in areas where the client is involved in heavy investment and consequently wishes to restrict the potential tenderers to those who are, in his opinion, less likely to jeopardise the completion date.

The clients in the latter category will retain a register of contractors, recording the extent of their normal operations and all information obtained as a result of previous experience or published reports.

The information will allow a long list of potential tenderers to be highlighted at the project-plan stage. On the basis that the client will be interested only in those contractors who currently have the interest and are technically sound and financially viable, a shortlist will be compiled. This will be achieved as a result of updating exercises. The principle to be followed is that a contractor should not be included on a tender list unless the client genuinely intends to award a contract to that contractor if the ensuing evaluation of tenders indicates that his tender is the most favourable. Contractors should not be given the financial risk of tendering in a pseudo-competitive exercise.

Care should be exercised at the tendering stage when including contractors who have a parent company. It is imperative to obtain a Parent Company Guarantee in these instances to safeguard the situations when a subsidiary may be tempted to default or the parent may be considering allowing the subsidiary to go into liquidation. This guarantee should be submitted by the contractor at the time of tender.

Buyers in the public sector and in some private utility undertakings in the electricity, gas, water and telecommunications sectors will need to take into account the requirements of the European Community Public Procurement Directives. The Directives which apply to certain high value contracts set out three ways in which contracts can be awarded, namely "open", "restricted" and "negotiated" procedures. For each of these, purchasers need to maintain records of their use of procedures other than open procedures.

Open procedures − any supplier may tender

Restricted procedures − any supplier may apply to be considered for inclusion on the tender list. The purchaser selects suppliers and invites them to tender

Negotiated procedures − direct discussions take place between the purchaser and one or more suppliers of the purchaser's choice.

Suppliers tendering or wishing to be invited to tender may need to meet conditions laid down by the buyer for inclusion on the tender list (known as "pre-qualification"). However the buyer must ensure these comply with public procurement laws. These conditions may include a requirement to provide evidence of their economic, financial or technical standing.

12.3.2 Contractor appraisal

The extent to which a company appraises contractors/suppliers depends on the resources and budget available to carry out the work involved. Major organisations make a full-time occupation of this activity and the contractors and suppliers questioned now expect regular approaches for extensive questionnaires to be completed − a time-consuming task. At the other end of the spectrum, however, a company may rely on a buyer's individual attitude to the sources of supply, without any attempt to assess the current capacity or financial stability. A decision has to be made therefore regarding the risk associated with the possibility of a contractor or supplier failing to meet his obligations regarding time of quality; will the consequences of a default be sufficiently high to justify an outlay at the pre-tender stage to ascertain the up-to-date technical and financial position of possible tenderers?

(a) **Information sources**

The client's own contractor register

Commercial directories

Government, local authorities or professional bodies' information departments

Previous employers

The best source is, of course, the contractor himself and in order to ensure that the information is presented by the contractor in an unambiguous manner it may well be advantageous to design a standard questionnaire form for completion.

(b) **Technical appraisal**

The information required will vary from project to project but it is likely that the following categories will contain adequate scope for comparison

Capability: management; technical resources; quality; attitude of operation; support from parent company or associates; location; industrial relations records.

What affiliations does the contractor have with trade federations or associations? is there a safety policy? does the work force operate within a national or local agreement?

Current capacity: facilities available; manpower and plant availability; limitations on finance

Past experience: for other companies; for client

Availability: interest; current commitments

Buyers need to be assured that their suppliers operate satisfactory quality-management systems. This should involve both parties to the contract in defining the systems to be operated, and in agreeing how these are controlled, tested and verified. The objective should be the achievement of Total Quality Management, the BSI definition of which is "the process for meeting customer expectations through continuing improvement in all areas of an organisation's operations, services and products".

The assessment of firms' quality systems in the United Kingdom is generally to ISO9000 (which is identical to the European Standard − EN29000 series) does not set out the characteristics of a particular product, but lists the key requirements of a quality system. These can be applied to almost any type of organisation. They include the need to establish a quality policy; to allocate responsibility clearly; to give authority to those allocated responsibility for quality; to document each stage of the production process; and to establish systems for identifying, remedying and preventing defects in quality.

A system of vendor appraisal/assessment using appraisal/assessment questionnaires similar to those illustrated in the Model Forms Appendix 1 and Appendix 2 which are based on questionnaires currently in use by major UK organisations ensures that suppliers/contractors are aware of the buyer's requirements. Clearly appraisal and assessment are time-consuming and expensive to both parties and should only be used if the value and/or volume or importance of the buyer's requirements is considered to be large enough. Appendix 1 (Appraisal) is a fairly simple method of obtaining information about a new potential supplier/contractor, but the buyer must remember it is time-consuming for the supplier/contractor to complete. The Appendix 1 form is normally sent to the supplier/contractor for them to complete and return to the buyer. Appendix 2 (Assessment) is far more complicated and expensive to both parties as it should involve the buyer sending a team of two or three persons (members of engineering/maintenance, purchasing and accounting) to the supplier's/contractor's premises for a full and in-depth evaluation of the supplier/contractor. Regular (every 12/24 months) updates of both appraisal and assessment information is necessary, particularly if the supplier/contractor is not ISO9000 registered.

(c) **Financial appraisal**

Unprofitable or under-financed companies can cause serious problems to a client and inadequate working capital may result in claims, non-performance, poor quality workmanship or even liquidation.

By ensuring that a contractor at least appears to be financially sound or has adequate support from a parent company then the risk of disruption to the work must be reduced; here again there are four areas of concern about which searching questions should be addressed:

Profitability: profits should grow in line with business. Companies which try to buy business by tendering below cost could be dangerous.

Turnover: rapid growth could lead to over-trading; declining turnover could lead to plant closure.

Net assets: ample reserves allow a contractor to make losses; new contractors have had insufficient time to build reserves. The three solutions for dealing with a contractor with insufficient funding are (1) obtain a parent company guarantee. (2) limit the size of the order. (3) remove it from the tender list.

Cash flow: cash is as important as profit and lack of it is more likely to cause bankruptcy.

(see Sections 4 and 6, pages 28 and 39 *et seq.* for expansion of this subject).

(d) **Overall appraisal**

The problem associated with acquiring large quantities of information is that it is soon outdated. Consequently, it will require renewing regularly, especially before the issue of enquiry documents or award of a contract.

The above technical information should receive a weighting, dependent on the risk associated with each individual item. Competitors can then be assessed on common ground prior to a decision being taken regarding the formation of a tender list.

The financial information should not be weighted. If a contractor has a financial problem, then he should be discarded without reference to the technical advantages.

(e) **Contractor performance records**

On completion of every contract, time should be taken by the client to complete a contractor's performance report noting the following details:

- i) Technical performance.
- ii) Management of the contract.
- iii) Administration performance eg accuracy of invoices.
- iv) General comments on cooperation, flexibility, incidence of claims.
- v) Industrial relations performance.
- vi) Safety record during the contract period.
- vii) Training of operatives.
- viii) Sub-contractor control.
- ix) Site organisation.
- x) Adherence to programme and progress reporting.
- xi) Did the contractor operate to Quality Procedure?

12.3.3   **Preparation of documents**

The contractor is at considerable risk at the tendering stage. If he included in the tender price a contingency for every risk that was allocated to him under the conditions of contract or specification he would never obtain any work in competition. The contractor therefore has to rely on the expertise of his staff to recognise the major areas of concern together with the legal and statutory obligations.

It is unusual for clients to allocate sufficient time for tendering that would allow contractors to assimilate every aspect of the enquiry, even though they will have been deemed to have done so under the conditions of contract. Consequently, it will be to both parties' advantage if the documents are prepared in a standard or recognisable format. Whilst familiarity may breed its own dangers, the contractor will at least be able to save time by knowing how to examine the documents. In addition if the enquiry is based on model documents with standard terminology then the contractor may feel entitled to expect the client to be consistent in his interpretation and adjudication of the meaning on contractual clauses.

12.3.4   **Basic enquiry documentation**

The magnitude of enquiry documentation will vary according to the value or element of risk associated with any contract. There is often a conflict between a desire to detail adequately the technical and commercial aspects of an enquiry and nevertheless control the thickness of documents and hence minimise the amount of time required by the tenderers to analyse the information.

All contracts will contain certain basic information regarding the specified conditions of contract, programme, prices and scope of work. These items could form the first four sections of standardised documentation as follows:

Part 1
'Form of Tender' or 'Form of Agreement' which will define the contract, giving the dates for commencement and completion of the work. The signatures required on this page make this section the 'legal' part.

Part 2
'Conditions of Contract' or 'Articles of Agreement', wherein all the commercial clauses are detailed.

Part 3
'Schedule of Prices'. This should be designed to ensure that it is the only section containing references to any prices or rates.

Part 4
'Scope of Work'. For larger contracts, the enquiry documentation could then be expanded to suit the particular contract by the inclusion of the following standard sections:

Part 5
'Administration Instructions' which could highlight any procedural aspect relating to administration: variation procedure, communications, incident reporting, quality assurance, contract closure procedure, etc.

Part 6
'Technical Specifications'. These would be the detailed components of the Scope of Work in Part 4.

Part 7
'Drawings'

Part 8
'Free-issue Materials'.

The introduction of the above standardised format in a company's contract documentation will ensure that, whatever the title of a contract, a person seeking pricing information, for example, will know that Part 3 will be the part to search.

12.3.5 Conditions of contract

It has been said often that conditions of contract are a means of highlighting areas of risk and allocating those risks either to the company or to the contractor. This allocation should be to the party which is best able either to control the risk or to estimate the effect to the risk. For instance, if we consider 'weather conditions or conditions caused by weather' to be a risk then, as neither party can control this item then the drafter of the conditions **may** allocate the risk to the contractor on the grounds that experience may enable the contractor to estimate the drop in productivity caused by weather conditions during certain periods of the year and certain locations that are covered by the contract.

A word of warning, however − it will be wrong to allocate any risk to the contractor if the company does not intend or will be unable to claim the redress associated with the risk if the situation occurs. Taking the previous example, if the company usually signs time sheets for a labour force of the contractor when weather dictates stoppage of work, then the risk must not be allocated to the contractor for him to price in his tender. This action would be wrong for three reasons:

- It results in double payment.
- It would be unfair to his competitors.
- The tenderers may be confused as to the method of tendering next time.

(a) Standard conditions of contract

Various institutions and trade associations have compiled conditions of contract to reflect their own operational areas and each endeavours to cover the complete spectrum of contracting activities in a manner that is fair to both the company (or the buyer/purchaser, client,or employer) and the contractor. In addition, many companies, nationalised industries, government departments and public service organisations devise their own model conditions to satisfy a need to cover differing operating conditions and attitudes. It is these different opinions and approaches to commercial and technical problems that cause tenderers to embark on risky paths if they choose to tender without understanding fully the philosophy behind the drafting of a particular set of conditions of contract.

The use of model or standard conditions therefore breeds uniformity of interpretations within each organisation and consequently reduces the risk to both parties. However, the drafter of contract documents must not assume that the model has removed the necessity for thought. Every contract will have varying areas of risk and the drafter must consider the relevance of every standard clause, detailing all replacement clauses in a 'special amendments' section to enable the tenderers to judge the effect of the changes. Any attempt by a trade association to require particular model conditions to be used or even to recommend them should be registered at the Office of Fair Trading under the Restrictive Trade Practices Act. Contact the OFT for futher information.

(b) **Specific conditions – minor services**
Many companies design special pre-printed pads of contract orders to deal with small-value contracts. The pads contain several carbon copies to cater for internal and external distribution and this reduces the administration involvement whilst covering sufficient of the risks anticipated in a small contract.

A favoured format for these pads is to restrict the front page to The Title and Contract Number

Part 1
'Form of Agreement' detailing the parties, definitions and programme.

Part 2
'Articles of Agreement' as printed overleaf.

Part 3
'Schedule of Prices', stating the price or referring to 'attached schedules'.

Part 4
'Scope of Work' continued on separate sheet if necessary

Signatures as necessary.

The Articles of Agreement would be detailed on the reverse side of all copies, covering the following headings:

Variation to the work
Method of payment
Safety requirements
Patents and other Intellectual Property
Confidential information
Responsibilities and indemnities

Insurance by contractor
Removal of contractor's personnel

The above list is often considered sufficient to cover the financial and practical risks involved.

(c) **Specific conditions – major fabrication works**
As a contrast to minor services, the potential risk to both the client and the contractor in a major fabrication contract is enormous. Consequently there is a need for greater expansion of the allocation of risk. Topics to be detailed may include:

Definitions
Parties' representatives
Manner of execution of work
Free-issue materials
Contractor to inform himself
Sub-contractors
Contractor's personnel
Variation to the work
Inspection and testing
Programme
Contractor's default
Force majeure
Suspension and termination
Guarantee of the work
Taxation, including certificates
Terms of payment
Audit rights
Liens
Ownership
Patents and other Intellectual Property Rights
Responsibility and indemnity
Insurance by contractor
Insurance by client
Permits, laws and regulations
Secrecy
Industrial relations
Business ethics
Safety
Law of contract
Notices

It will be seen therefore that the range of applicable clauses is extensive and the document must be well planned to protect both parties.

12.3.6 **Issue of enquiry documents**

It is common practice for the enquiry inviting tenders to consist of:

Covering letter explaining the invitation and stipulating the date and time by which tenders must be delivered.

Instructions to tenderers giving details of the manner in which the tender should be submitted.

The enquiry documents referred to in paragraph 12.3.4, above.

Pre-printed labels for the return of tenders.

From this point onwards a strict ethical discipline should be followed in all aspects of the tendering and contracting activities. No tenderer should be given information or assistance that has not been made available to all tenderers. For tenders under the public procurement rules there are strict rules on this. The period of time for tendering should be realistic and should not be extended unless it becomes obvious that the competitive element of the enquiry will be jeopardised. Continual relaxation of tendering periods creates precedents which may be difficult to overcome. Any extensions however should be granted to all tenderers.

During the tendering exercise, any requests for clarification or additional information must be dealt with in a form that can be transmitted to all tenderers. A question-and-answer format is ideal for this purpose.

13 Pre-contract stage

13.1 **Receipt of tenders**

A contractor is entitled to expect that his tender will receive consideration and that any information which he includes in his tender will remain confidential and will not be disclosed to any party which is not involved in the evaluation of tenders.

Consequently the purchasing company, its staff, and the contractor can all be protected by the introduction of and adherence to a procedure for dealing with tenders which will limit the awareness of the confidential information by standardising the manner in which tenders are received, evaluated and awarded. The usual presumption of confidentiality is waived in some cases of purchasing by public sector organisations and some private utilities which are subject to EU/GATT requirements, necessitating publication of details of prices received (See paragraph 13.3, below).

This objective can be achieved if:
Tenders are stored in locked cabinets until the tender opening takes place.

Where tender documentation is submitted electronically, which is increasingly common and saves paper and postage delays, the use of passwords should be introduced to ensure confidentiality. The parties may also wish to send the data electronically in encoded form.

The opening of tenders is witnessed and a record of prices signed by those persons present.

The communications with tenderers are of a formal nature only.

Any unsolicited communication from tenderers does not form part of the evaluation of tenders if the revised offer is in effect a reduction in price or programme. (The revision could, however, be accepted if that tenderer is being awarded the contract for other reasons.)

Late tenders are returned to the tenderer unopened.

Faxed tenders are discouraged.

13.2 Evaluation of tenders

Two initial appraisals of tenders should be carried out before any contact is made with the tenderers: a technical appraisal, often carried out without the schedule of prices information, and secondly a commercial appraisal that combines the contractual and financial aspects. The amalgamation of the technical and commercial opinions enables the tenders to be brought to a comparable basis in line with the purchaser's requirements. Both appraisals will have taken account of qualifications or deficiencies by including in the evaluation estimates of cost for each omission or excess.

It is at this stage that the evaluators will include the effects of any criteria relating to the manner in which it is anticipated that the contractor will carry out the work. Perhaps it is known that his managing skills are deficient in the area of planning or quality control which will necessitate a greater degree of client participation. This participation costs money and an estimate should be added to the tender price for comparison purposes. These latter criteria, if known, should be registered with the the tender-opening panel prior to the receipt of tenders thus minimising the possibility of an unfair judgement after the price levels are known.

In order to finalise the decision-making, the evaluating team should decide whether there is a need to approach any tenderer for clarification or discussion. The meetings should not be used as a lever to obtain unfair concessions or a manipulation of the order of tendering. Unethical approaches may gain savings in the short term but this would be at the expense of the competitors; credibility in the market place would fall, and a dangerous precedent be established.

On the other hand a reservation by a tenderer on a fundamental point of commercial or technical significance may justify the disqualification of the tenderer by the company on the grounds that the reduced risk acceptance by the tenderer may jeopardise the project objectives.

13.3 Post-tender negotiation

It is the aim of every purchasing professional to conclude the best deal for his organisation when obtaining goods or services. This should be done within the framework of the policies of the Codes of Ethics of the buying organisation and the Institute.

There are various techniques which a purchaser might use to reduce the cost of goods or services towards this end. One is to enter into discussion and possibly negotiation with tenderers after the receipt of tenders. This has come to be known as Post-Tender Negotiation (PTN) and has attracted much attention after the Report on Government Purchasing (1984) recommended its use by government departments.

The subsequent publicity has given rise to a number of misconceptions and a deal of confusion. So what is Post-Tender Negotiation? The CIPS defines PTN as:

"Negotiation after receipt of formal tenders and before the letting of contract(s) with supplier(s)/contractor(s) submitting the lowest acceptable tender(s) with a view to obtaining an improvement in price, delivery or content, in circumstances which do not put other tenderers at a disadvantage or affect adversely their confidence or trust in the competitive system."

It is probably easier to state what PTN is not! As an aid to dispelling this confusion, the following exemplify situations where PTN does not apply:

- a formal tendering procedure is not in use and "tender" is used loosely to describe quotations which are subject to negotiation.

- the buyer has stated before initial tenders are invited that a second tender will or may be called for, based on either the initial description of the requirement or a modified one.

- there is only one supplier for a given item and it is logical to negotiate with him from the outset whether or not a tendering process has been used.

- discussions are held to clarify technical or contractual matters necessary for a proper evaluation of tenders.

- it is used as a way of short-cutting pre-tender preparations and providing a means whereby errors and omissions can be corrected post-tender.

- a price adjustment is requested by a tenderer after the submission of tenders. In this case the original price should be that on which the tender is considered, but in the event of it being accepted the contract sum will be the lower amount offered.

- obvious errors in totalling extensions or calculations are corrected by the buyer.

- after a contract has been made, either party to it negotiates with a view to varying the contract.

- the buyer attempts to reduce prices in the absence of a reasoned case for so doing.

Organisations using formal competitive tendering procedures in their purchasing activities have well established procedures which provide the transparency and audit trail needed to satisfy accountability requirements and suppliers are accustomed to operating within this framework.

The term PTN may be seen by some to be an opportunity to extract by unethical means, purchasing power or political influence, a better bargain than would otherwise have been available. This is not Post-Tender Negotiation which is rather a kind of negotiation to ensure that the buying organisation obtains true value for money by purchasing an acceptable product or service at a competitive but fair market price (not necessarily the cheapest) within the time required.

Whatever the nature of the buying organisation, whatever purchasing practices or techniques are employed, **there should be no Dutch auction, horse trading or coercion** in an attempt to reduce prices in the absence of a reasoned case for so doing.

Perfect competition where the tender and specification issued by the buyer are matched in every way by the tenderer may not always be possible in practice. This is known by both parties. Joint action after the receipt of tenders permits clarification and discussion to proceed, possibly through negotiation, to a balanced and professional evaluation. This is ethical and correct when part of an evaluation process but it does impose a strict discipline on both parties to define what is required and what is offered in reply.

When a buying organisation has decided that it will conduct PTN, it is suggested that the following matters should be considered for inclusion in the relevant operating procedures:

- what criteria should be considered before a decision to conduct PTN is made?

- the value of the contract, potential for savings, and the cost to the buyer of conducting PTN, against the likely improvements

- is there time to conduct PTN without delaying the completion date for the contract?

- effect on the future supply situation

- is the contract affected by regulations such as EC Directives and GATT which require equality of treatment of potential suppliers? PTN is normally prohibited for public procurement contract in this category - contact the Home Office which is in charge of this area, for further information.

- is it or would it be considered to be ethical by the public and by competing tenderers?

The controls needed to govern the use of PTN can include:

- who will authorise PTN in particular cases and how will the person relate to the person authorised to award the contract?

- who will take part in and who will lead the negotiation?

- who will award the contract?

- what documentation is needed to record events before, during and after PTN and does this provide a satisfactory audit trail?

- how will the conduct and results of PTN be reviewed and by whom?

13.4 Award of contract

The award can be evidenced in several ways but the two usual documents are either a letter of acceptance where the purchaser accepts an offer or an amended offer, or a form of agreement signed by both parties. In the former case, it is quite likely that the letter of acceptance will list all the documents, tender, amendments, minutes of meetings and correspondence that combine to make the contract. The form of agreement however will be the entire agreement and any variations to the original enquiry documents will have been incorporated into the revised agreement before signature.

The contractor should not be allowed to commence work until the contract has been established or signed. Experience has shown that the urgency and genuine intent to finalise the documentation disappears if the contractor is given an early written or oral instruction to proceed with the work.

13.5 Debriefing

A formal letter of regret should be sent to all unsuccessful tenderers as soon as possible after the contract has been acknowledged. This should take place before any publicity has been authorised regarding the award.

The regret letter, however, often promotes enquiries into the reasons for not accepting an offer. Care should be taken not to disclose information regarding pricing levels for several reasons. Firstly, it confirms the pricing philosophy of competitors. Secondly, the information may lead to deeper discussions into the possibilities of alternatives that could have been offered and this is a waste of time. Thirdly, it will not achieve the result of helping the contractor to tender more competitively next time because nobody will know how the competitors will react next time. It is far better to restrict comments to areas of technicality if this will be beneficial to the purchaser in the future, or else refuse to discuss the issue.

14 Post-contract-award stage

14.1 Contract administration

Having established a contract, a project team will soon be aware of any shortfall in its contract planning:

> Is the project still on programme?
> Does the specification still reflect the company's needs?
> Was the form of contract correct?
> Have the adminstration procedures been detailed?
> How will variations be priced and authorised?
> Will the company still be able to supply information or free-issue materials on time?
> Are there sufficient incentives in the contract for the contractor?
> What does the contract say about 'limits of liability', 'contractor's default' and 'delay in completion?'
> What work has to be completed for each interim payment?

The contract is an agreement between the company and the contractor. Alterations to the terms and conditions of the contract therefore require the agreement of both parties in the form of an amendment to contract unless the contract specifically provides for some other method.

In most contracts the clauses or article headed 'variations' give the company the unilateral right to authorise alterations to the job specification subject only to the constraint that, at the time of authorising the variation, the financial basis of evaluation to be used to compensate the contractor must be stated. For the practical administration of large site contracts, the variation procedure includes the use of site instructions for small alterations to the work. It is important to distinguish between the different type of 'alterations' and how they are handled:

> Changes in contract conditions involve 'amendments to contract'
> Changes in job specification will involve 'variations'
> Changes in 'instructions to contractor' can be by letter or otherwise in writing.

14.2 Amendments to contract

It must be a condition in the articles of agreement that any alterations to the contract, other than to the job specification, must be made in writing and agreed by both parties.

Thus, if one party wishes to alter a term of the articles of agreement, or the schedule of prices, this must be done with the agreement of the other party, and must be formally recorded as an amendment to contract.

14.3 Variations to the work

(a) General

The contract must be drafted to ensure that the client has the right to vary the work and that the contractor has an obligation to accommodate those changes. Consequently the contract must also include the procedure for agreeing the effects of any variation in relation to cost, time and quality. It is quite likely that the contract will limit the right to vary the work to a 'percentage of the contract price' above which the agreement of the contractor would have to be obtained.

There are two aspects of controlling variations. One is an in-house change control system and the other is the mechanism for dealing with the contract.

The objective of the internal control is to ensure that, whilst no opportunity to improve project profitability is missed, only beneficial changes are implemented. These can be identified only after the impact on the current and associated contracts within the project framework has been assessed. This can be achieved by:

> Imposing a formal discipline through the procedure on anybody proposing a variation to investigate thoroughly and quantify the consequences and predictions.
> Requiring a justification based on project economics.
> Limiting change authorisation to those who have an overview of all aspects involved.

Changes are caused by many factors: statutory bodies, certification authorities and environmentalists, internal mistakes, or improvements to avoid obsolescence. But the greatest cause is the lack of time and thought given to the preparation of the specification, and the lack of time allocated at the evaluation of the tenders to understand what the tenderers are offering.

(b) **Variation procedure**
The procedure should centre around a 4-part form:

Part 1 − details the client's proposed change or refers to an accompanying scope of work.

Part 2 − is completed by the contractor within a stipulated period, giving the cost and time implications.

Part 3 − is the formal notification to the contractor to proceed with the variation.

Part 4 − records the cost and time effect on the contract and would be signed by both parties.

The variation forms could be incorporated in carbonised copy pads to ease distribution.

14.4 Site instructions

The variation procedure may provide for minor variations, which the contractor accepts have no effect on the programme or do not exceed a small value, to be authorised by means of a site work instruction. At regular intervals, site instructions will be gathered together and put under one variation.

A site instruction is a written instruction issued to the contractor during the work, and must not include matters that should be the subject of an amendment to contract or variation order.

Site instructions may relate to such items as:

Authorisation to proceed with a limited amount of work (eg on dayworks);
Clarification of a contract or technical requirement;
Early release of additional information, eg provision of an equipment specification pending release of updated drawings, etc.

14.5 Time of completion

Even in the simplest projects, the works will consist of several sections, some of which are operationally dependent on others. Thus, there will be a logical sequence in which completion of each will be required in order to achieve satisfactory completion of the whole project. It is essential that the definition of completion should be as precise as possible as any sanction or incentive in respect of adherence to an agreed programme will be related to completion.

It may be to the client's advantage, within limits, to bring forward the date of completion by additional expenditure. By controlling the expenditure during a reimbursable contract the client can also control its execution by requesting the contractor to accelerate the work if this can be achieved by spending more in particular ways.

The contractor has an obligation to keep to the agreed programme and the client must take care that actions on the part of the client do not relieve the contractor of this obligation.

There are several ways in which the terms of payment can give the contractor an incentive to early completion.

Where the contract is on a lump-sum basis for carrying out site work, the contractor's overheads will have been estimated on the assumption of the site work lasting a given period of time. Any over-run on that time will cost the contractor money.

Where payment is at defined rates for units of completed work then unless progress is achieved to programme, the contractor will still have to pay out the costs for hire of plant overheads and wages of direct labour, but he will not be recovering these costs on the cash-flow basis on which he prepared his tender.

If the contract price or a proportion of it is withheld until completion is achieved, then any delay will cost the contractor interest charges and lose him working capital.

All these incentives are negative ones and, whilst they have some effect, the carrot is often more effective than the stick. The difficulty is to make certain that the carrot really produces greater effort on the part of the contractor. Before offering a bonus, therefore, it is necessary to establish the norm both in time and price. A bonus is something to be negotiated after tenders have been received, not something to be mentioned when tenders are invited.

Particular care has to be taken when negotiating a bonus and penalty clause for a cost-reimbursable contract, the danger being that, to earn the bonus, the contractor will spend the client's money to an unreasonable extent. It is essential therefore to relate the bonus and penalty provisions not only to time but also to the excess of actual costs over target.

Whilst, in terms of damages, it is reasonable to grant extensions of time for delays beyond the contractor's reasonable control, the same considerations do not apply to the bonus payment. The client is only interested in paying for results, thus extensions of time as regards bonus should be allowed only where delays are due to acts or omissions of the client.

It is part of the main contractor's job to organise his sub-contracting in the most effective manner and on the most favourable terms. Even if the sub-contractor does accept a fixed completion period coupled with damages for delay, such damages will always be related to the sub-contract price thus leaving a gap between the main contractor's liability to the client and what can be recovered from the sub-contractor. This is part of the main contractor's risk for which he earns a margin on the sub-contract price. There have been many arguments regarding nominated sub-contractors. However, provided that the main contractor is given the opportunity to object to nominations prior to the letting of the sub-contract, there is no reason to treat these sub-contracts differently from any others.

14.6 Extension to contract period

Generally contracts can be divided into these primary categories:

Contracts where the contractor supplies services, or makes personnel available, as and when required by the company.

Contracts (usually construction-related) where the contractor undertakes to carry out a defined scope of work in an agreed period of time.

14.6.1 Extensions – time not critical

For service contracts, there is usually no obligation on the contractor to carry out a particular service in a fixed period of time, as his rate of progress is dependent upon the numbers of his personnel required by the company. The contract period is therefore the period during which he has agreed to supply his services and for which he has fixed his rates and prices.

Any extension to the contract period for service contracts will therefore be an extension of the date until which the contractor has agreed to supply his services, and may require a negotiated change in rates and prices to allow for cost changes. These changes will then be the subject of an amendment to contract.

14.6.2 Extension of time-critical contracts

If the contractor requires extension to the contract period other than those agreed for variations to the work, the contractor must submit an application accordingly. The application may be for such reasons as:

Force majeure;

Events outside the control of the contractor;

Acts of the company delaying the work;

Changes of method and sequence of working imposed on the contractor;

Variations to work scope for which an adjustment to the contract period cannot be agreed;

Cumulative effect of variations;
Late delivery of free-issue materials.

All such applications should be treated as contract 'claims'.

14.7 Claims

A claim is a request from either party to a contract for an alleged entitlement under the contract that is not automatically being granted to him. It is usually confined to payment of additional moneys or an allowance for additional time for the performance of the work.

A claim will often occur as a result of:

An unforeseen loss or expense, which may arise out of disputes on the interpretation and meaning of contract clauses.
Disputes as to what is included in the contract price.
Breaches of contract by either party.

A request from the contractor for additional payment outside the terms of the contract may include requests for escalation payments in excess of the formula (if any) specified in the contract or a relaxation of terms of payment or incentive payments not included in the original contract. These requests are for *ex-gratia* payments and should be resisted.

For claims to be considered, they must meet all the following conditions:

They should be based on the true effect on the contractor of the events concerned;
They should include only those items which an experienced contractor could not reasonably have been expected to anticipate, or did not have an opportunity to include in his price.
They should be allowable under the terms and conditions of the contract.

The detailed submission of a claim by the contractor should include the information set out under the heading above and should state the clause in the contract under which the claim is being submitted. Any claims from sub-contractors or suppliers employed by the contractor should not be submitted directly to the company. Such claims should be received by the contractor and, if he wishes to proceed in the matter, he should himself make appropriate submission to the company.

It is vital that, once agreement has been reached on a claim, the details should be recorded in writing and signed by both parties. It is also important that the note of the settlement should state very clearly what is included and what is excluded. For example, the settlement may be made during the 'defects liability' period and would therefore exclude any further liabilities of the contractor in that respect. Or, it may be made at a time when work is still going on under variation orders and would, therefore, obviously exclude that work. It should also be noted, if the contract included a price-variation clause, whether claims under that clause are included or not.

There is only one time at which to record the settlement and that is at the meeting at which the settlement has been reached. It should be done there and then since, if it is left, it may be delayed for some time, and people may then genuinely disagree on what was 'agreed' or may have second thoughts and might attempt to set aside the agreement by disputing what was or was not included.

14.8   Defects, damage and injury

If, during the course of the contract, the engineer decides that any work carried out by the contractor is defective or does not comply with the contract, then it is usual to provide that he requires the contractor to take corrective action, if necessary re-execute the work, or take away defective items and replace them with ones which do comply with the contract. In case the contractor fails to replace defective work, most forms of contract provide for the client to have the right to do the work himself and charge the contractor the reasonable additional cost incurred. Any action so taken by the client should not affect the client's right to claim the damages for delay. Thus, not only must the contractor pay the costs of putting the work right, he almost certainly faces the prospect of paying damages for delay when the works are finally completed. Whether there is any limit on such liability depends on the contract terms.

The main contractor should also be fully responsible for defects caused by his sub-contractors and suppliers, as if it were his own work. Where the client is claiming against the main contractor because of defects in a sub-contract he must resist the temptation to deal with the sub-contractor directly. Such action would not only make the main contractor's position impossible, it might well prejudice any contractual rights the client has against the main contractor.

It might be expected that, where a client places a contract with a contractor, then the liability for any accident or injury arising out of the execution of the contract would rest with the contractor. Unfortunately for the client the position is not quite as simple as this. It is true that if the work the contractor is employed to do can lawfully be done with risk of damage and injury resulting, then, in the absence of negligence and provided that the client has engaged a competent and experienced contractor and given him control over the carrying out of the contract, it is the contractor who will be liable for the consequences of any possible injury or damage to third parties.

However, where the contract work is of a kind that clearly involves the risk of damage to property or injury to persons, eg a demolition contract, then the fact that the client has given someone else the authority to execute the work cannot relieve him of responsibility for the consequences of an accident. The client is also liable if a nuisance, in the legal sense of the term, is created on his property, like smoke or excessive noise from construction operations.

The client should therefore ensure that, where the damage or injury arises out of the contractor's default, it is the contractor and not the client who has to meet the claim from the third party. Thus the client should obtain an indemnity in the contract under which the contractor indemnifies the client against any claims made against the client and for any costs, damages or expenses (including legal fees) which the client may be called upon to pay. It must be remembered, however, that such an indemnity in no way lessens the client's legal liability and the third party is free to pursue a valid claim against the client. The client must therefore ensure that the contractor has adequate resources available, by insurances or other means, to implement the terms of the indemnity and obtain a parent company, or directors' personal guarantee for greater protection.

Insurance policies are technical documents of considerable complexity and it requires an expert in insurance to check that the policy is in conformity with the terms of the contract.

14.9 Security for performance

A client is entitled to require security from the contractor for the performance of his contract. The primary purpose of such security is to provide the client with adequate funds to meet the costs of bringing in another firm to undertake the work should the contractor be seriously in default. Additionally if the client makes the contractor an advance payment at the beginning of the contract he needs security for the repayment of that amount if the contractor defaults and during the Defects Liability Period the client needs to retain a security against the contractor's not returning to rectify defects.

Traditionally the forms of bond in use in the UK have been ones under which the client's right to recover payment have been limited to situations in which the parties have agreed upon the damages payable as a result of the contractor's default or there has been judgement against the contractor either in the courts or at arbitration.

In practice such bonds are of little value to the client other than in a situation in which the contractor is in liquidation and even then the client must expect a substantial delay before he obtains payment under the bond thus leaving him with a cash-flow problem.

For these reasons, and also because they can be more effectively used to bring pressure on contractors to perform, UK clients are increasingly turning to the use of "on-demand" bonds which have been commonly used in international practice for a number of years.

Under these bonds the client can call the bond on first demand and **without having to prove any default on the part of the contractor.** The position of a bank giving such a bond has been stated by Lord Denning in these words.

> "A bank which gives a performance guarantee must honour that guarantee according to its terms. It is not concerned in the least with the relations between the supplier and the customer; nor with the question whether the supplier has performed his contracted obligations or not; nor with the question whether the supplier is in default or not. The bank must pay according to its guarantee on demand, if so stipulated, without proof or conditions. The only exception is, when there is clear fraud, of which the bank has notice."

Although there has been reference to the issue of fraud in all cases which have come before the courts on the question of enforcement of performance bonds there has been no case in which fraud has been established to the court's satisfaction. It appears however that it would be necessary to show that the client had made a demand under the bond to the bank knowing it to be invalid but representing to the bank that it was valid. Further it would need to be established that the bank knew of the fraud or that the only reasonable inference from the facts was that the demand was fraudulent.'

Only very exceptionally is it likely that these requirements will be met and for all practical purposes a contractor who has provided an "on-demand" bond has to accept that the bond may be called without his having any right to prevent this from happening. That would not of course prevent the contractor from subsequently claiming from the client for the repayment of the money which he will have had to pay to the bank under his counter-guarantee if he considers that the demand was wrongful, but it would be for him to prove that such was the case.

The value to the client of such a bond is obvious and must be his preferred choice. Provided that the client takes a responsible attitude towards the calling of the bond and the contractor has adequate recourse to the courts or arbitration if the demand is in fact unjustified, it is not considered that the contractor is put under an unreasonable risk. His practical problem is that the total value of such "on-demand" bonds will be deducted by the bank from his overdraft limit and may therefore impede his ability to tender for new work.

Where the bond is to cover the advance payment then it would be reasonable to provide that it should be reduced as this payment is recovered but the administrative work involved in so doing means that such reduction should probably only be done, say, quarterly.

Parent company guarantees

If goods are being purchased from a subsidiary company of a group and more particularly if the supplier is simply a UK sales company of an overseas manufacturer and has probably no assets in its own name, then the client ought to obtain a guarantee from the parent company in respect of all liabilities and obligations of the subsidiary.

14.10 Retention money

A less contentious and therefore seemingly less expensive method of safeguarding performance is retention money and this concept would have been built into the original terms-of-payment clause in the contract. Part, usually five per cent of each payment due to the contractor, is retained by the client until the contractor has fulfilled his obligations under the contract. Half of the money so retained is released upon completion of the works and the balance released at the end of the defects liability period.

The term 'less expensive' is used because, in practice, this might not prove to be so at the end of the day. Retention money provides no protection to a client who has parted with an advance payment for a project that never really gets off the ground. On the other hand, most contractors work on low margins and rely for their profits on turning their money over fast. Allowing the usual time lag in certification and payment there will normally be not less than six weeks' work completed on site for which payment has not been made. On a contract lasting, say, 24 months this would mean that, on average, work to the value of at least five per cent of the contract had been executed but not paid for. In addition to this constraint upon the contractor's cash flow, when payment is rendered a further five per cent of the sum due is retained by the client as security for performance by the contractor. This cumulative effect has led to the allegation by contractors that the clients apply retention-money provisions, regardless of the complexity of the works, as a means of cheap finance.

The highest cost to the contractor of retention moneys lies in the money retained during the defects liability period. Where the works are completed and taken over in sections the retention moneys should be released on a sectional basis.

14.11 Contract closure

Every story must have an ending and the contracting story is no exception. In this book there has been great emphasis on the need for a high standard of planning, contract documentation and contract administration. It is equally necessary for there to be evidence that the contract has been completed to everybody's satisfaction. This entails a two-part exercise: first an internal procedure to ascertain that all involved departments have no outstanding items and secondly written evidence signed by both parties that the contract is ended with the exception of on-going liabilities of the contractor relating to secrecy, patents and other intellectual property rights, and statutory periods of limitation.

The purpose of the closure procedure is to provide a formal mechanism for administering the closure of the contract after the end of any retention or guarantee period, and after all other matters have been resolved, and specifically to:

Ensure completion of the administration formalities, as quickly as possible, whilst keeping all interested functions informed.

Record that all technical matters that require to be done before closing the contract have in fact been carried out.

Determine the extent to which liquidated damages (when applicable) may be deducted from the contract price.

Record the end of the retention period and any guarantee period (when applicable) in accordance with the contract, and to record the date of the final inspection of the work before expiry of such periods.

Record the date of release of retention or bank guarantee (when applicable).

Obtain a complete statement of any specific limits on the contractual obligations that continue after completion of the work or service, and on any obligations that continue after the end of the guarantee or maintenance period.

Record the result of a materials reconciliation.

Record the process of finalising contract payments.

Summarise claims made against or received from the contractor.

Record a summary of the financial payments made and received in relation to the contract.

On completion of the above exercise, agreement will have been reached between the parties on all commercial and technical aspects of the contract. To bring the contract formally to conclusion requires only the signatures of both parties to a document which records the acceptance of the work by the client and the price paid or to be paid to the contractor, and certifies that all obligations under the contract have been fulfilled. Generally, such a document is referred to in the contract as the 'Final Certificate'.

Part Three:
Model Conditions of Contract

This part of the book is devoted to model conditions, each of which is tailored to meet the requirements of a particular area of purchasing or contracting. No one set of conditions can adequately cover a purchasing function ranging from, say, the supply of moulding powders to the supply, delivery and erection of a large machine.

The model conditions should be treated as examples only. They are all quite short and simple and many contracts will require much more detailed conditions. They should be regarded more as an *aide memoire* or skeleton from which more detailed contractual conditions can be drafted and negotiated from. They are largely drafted from the point of view of the buyer - for example title passes to goods on delivery whereas a seller would want title to pass on payment. However they seek to achieve a reasonable balance - e.g. the seller's liability for consequential losses is often excluded, whereas a buyer expecting a contract to be heavily negotiated may wish to start from a position where such liability is not excluded and work down to that position in negotiations. Another exmple of a less balanced contract would be the buyer that removed the force majeure clause (which normally is there to protect the supplier or seller).

Each order should be thought of as a separate contract and the model conditions looked at to see if they require any modification or amplification. To aid the buyer in his deliberation each set of model conditions is **preceded** by guidance notes setting out how the conditions tie up with the order, and detailing points to which the buyer should give particular attention. These guidance notes should be read before starting to draw up a particular contract.

Guidance notes on the use of Model One:

'Conditions of Contract for Engineering Plant and Materials
(Exclusive of Erection)'

1 **Use**

Use for **Supply and delivery** *only* of engineering materials and equipment.

2 **General note on negotiation**

Always specify in the enquiry that it is a condition of the order that these Conditions are to be accepted. If the Seller raises any objections these can then be the basis for negotiation. Avoid attempting to amend the Seller's conditions to meet the Buyer's requirements (see Part One, Section 1.4).

3 **Definition of requirements**

The following information should be part of any enquiry and/or purchase order:

3.1 Quantity, description and specification (eg British, European or International, drawing number etc.) of goods required.

3.2 Delivery date(s); be specific (see Part One, Section 5 − Seller's Default).

3.3 Delivery point.

3.4 Terms of payment, including retention money (if any) (see note 4.3).

3.5 Whether price is fixed or subject to a price-adjustment formula (see note 4.3.3).

3.6 Liquidated damages (if any) (see Part One, Section 5.2).

3.7 Whether subject to the Buyer's inspection and expediting.

3.8 Fabrication programme (if required) including dates when design and detail information and any 'free-issue' items must be available.

3.9 Details of specification, test certificates, performance tests and guarantees.

3.10 Stipulate any restrictions to be imposed on sub-letting.

3.11 State any special or unusual requirements and any special markings required on materials or equipment.

3.12 Specify any material which is to be of 'free-issue' (see note 4.6).

3.13 Any special protection, packing or transport requirements.

4 Notes on certain clauses

4.1 Clauses 2 and 8 − 'Quality' and 'Acceptance':
Where possible, it is advisable to specify in detail the purpose for which the goods are required and the varying circumstances under which they will be required to operate. Consideration should be given to the degree of losses which could be incurred should the goods fail to perform to specification.

4.2 Clause 5− 'Passing of property and risk to Buyer':
Make the seller responsible for delivery to the required site. An 'ex-works' offer should not normally be agreed.

In the latter case property and risk pass to the Buyer when goods are placed at Buyer's disposal. The Buyer will not only have to pay for transport but may also find it necessary to arrange special insurance cover against damage or loss in transit. See the provisions of Part One, Section 4, with regard to the relationship between the passing of property and stage payments.

4.3 Clause 6 − 'Terms of payment': (see Part One, Section 4):
The terms of payment *must* be specified on the order, including retention money (if any).

4.3.1 For important items of equipment it is recommended that some money should be retained until the end of the warranty period as 'insurance' against the Seller not fulfilling his obligations under the contract, eg performance tests, warranty etc.

4.3.2 Where stage payments have to be agreed these should be related to and be conditional upon work done. See the provisions of Part One, Section 4, with regard to payments in advance of delivery.

4.3.3 Although it is the recommended practice to obtain a 'fixed price', it may be more economical in the case of high-value, extended-delivery items, to agree a price subject to a price-adjustment formula. This may work out cheaper than a 'pre-loaded' firm price. In such cases the BEAMA CPA System is recommended (see Part One, Section 4.7).

4.4 Clause 7 — 'Loss or damage in transit':
It is usual for the Seller to require notification of loss or damage in such a manner as to comply with the carrier's conditions. However, the Buyer is not party to the contract between the Seller and the carrier and cannot therefore reasonably be deemed to know of, or to have accepted, the terms of that contract. The model clause should be acceptable to the majority of suppliers.

4.5 Clause 11 — 'Force majeure' (see Part One, Section 5.5).

4.5.1 The Buyer should not pay cancellation charges losses should be where they fall. The Buyer should only pay an equitable sum in respect of cancellation charges, taking account of the loss that may be incurred by both parties and the degree to which such losses are insurable. The Seller should be covered by insurance in respect of consequential losses, eg loss of profits, loss of other contracts, interruption of business etc. and fire or explosion at the Seller's works. Negotiations should therefore be restricted to costs in respect of materials and labour actually expended up to the date of cancellation.

4.5.2 The Seller is not entitled to impose any additional charges in respect of the storage of goods during a force majeure situation unless there is provision for such extra charges in the terms of the contract.

4.5.3 Remember, a delivery extension granted under a force majeure situation also extends the period before which liquidated damages (if any) are payable.

4.5.4 With regard to the imposition of supply by allocation due to force majeure circumstances every endeavour should be made by the Buyer to obtain an assurance from the Seller that all his customers are allocated goods on an equal basis. If any of the goods are being manufactured or processed by the Seller — whether for his own use or for sale — albeit at a reduced rate due to force majeure, the imposition of allocations is not itself covered by the definition of force majeure since the choice of the customer/user *is* under the Seller's control and at his own discretion.

4.5.5 Where a price is established relative to a given quantity, no variation in that price basis should be allowed if the Buyer is forced to take a reduced quantity due to a declaration of force majeure.

4.6 Clause 18 – 'Free-issue materials':
Where the order provides for a significant amount of free-issue materials consideration should be given to the use of the Special Conditions detailed in Part One, Section 7, to protect the Buyer and allow him to retrieve his materials should the Seller find himself in financial difficulties.

4.7 Clause 19 – 'Warranty': (see Part One, Section 1.7).

4.7.1 This clause defines liabilities. Sellers' liability is limited to reasonably foreseeable losses. Some sellers will insist on a cap on liability and exclusion of damages for loss of profit.

4.7.2 Practicalities to be considered and agreed are:

– Who pays for the return of the defective goods to Seller?
– What is an acceptable time to be allowed for repair or replacement of goods?
– If service call required, are all costs covered by Warranty, ie callout, parts and labour?
– Can service be called for out of normal working hours, ie during the night, weekends and Bank Holidays?
– Is a maintenance contract (to follow the warranty period) being contemplated – negotiate before placing the procurement contract.

4.7.3 There is no legal reqirement for a Buyer to limit the warranty period in time to 12 months or whatever.

4.8 Clause 20 – 'Insolvency and Bankruptcy':
This clause reflects the Insolvency Act 1985 which introduced 'administrative receiver' and 'administrator' appointed by a Court. Among the reasons for appointing an administrator are:

1 to continue the company in whole or in part
2 to optimise assets for liquidation.

5 Overseas application
These model conditions may be adapted for use with overseas sources of supply by reference to Part One, Section 9.

6 Terms of payment
It is advisable to consider including a specific clause defining the time and method of payment, usually within a defined number of days of receipt of a valid invoice.

Model One

Conditions of Contract for Engineering Plant and Materials (Exclusive of Erection)

1 Definitions

1.1 'Buyer' means the person, firm or company so named in the Purchase Order.

1.2 'Seller' means the person, firm or company to whom the Purchase Order is issued and named on it.

1.3 'Goods' means all goods covered by the Purchase Order including raw materials, processed materials or fabricated products and listed on the Purchase Order.

1.4 'Purchase Order' means Buyer's Purchase Order which specifies that these conditions apply to it.

1.5 'The Contract' means the contract between the Buyer and Seller consisting of the Purchase Order, these conditions and any other documents (or parts thereof) specified in the Purchase Order. Should there be any inconsistency between the documents comprising the Contract they shall have precedence in the order herein listed.

2 Quality

In the absence of a specification referred to on the Purchase Order or sample, all goods supplied shall be of satisfactory quality and fit for their purpose.

3 Delivery date

The date of delivery of goods shall be that specified in the Purchase Order unless agreed otherwise between Buyer and Seller. Seller shall furnish such programmes of manufacture and delivery as Buyer may reasonably require and Seller shall give notice to Buyer as soon as practicable if such programmes are or are likely to be delayed.

4 Incorrect delivery

All goods must be delivered at the delivery point specified in the Purchase Order.

If goods are incorrectly delivered, Seller will be held responsible for any additional expense incurred in delivering them to their correct destination.

5 Passing of property and risk to Buyer

The property and risk in the goods shall remain in Seller until they are delivered at the point specified in the Purchase Order.

6 Terms of payment

Unless otherwise stated in the Purchase Order, payment will be made within 28 days of receipt and agreement of invoice.

Value Added Tax, where applicable, shall be shown separately on all invoices as a strictly nett extra charge.

7 Loss or damage in transit

7.1 Buyer shall advise Seller and the carrier (if any) in writing, otherwise than by a qualified signature on any Delivery Note, of any loss or damage within the following time limits:

1 Partial loss, damage, defects or non-delivery of any separate part of a consignment shall be advised within seven days of date of delivery of the consignment or part consignment.

2 Non-delivery of whole consignment shall be advised within 21 days of notice of despatch.

7.2 Seller shall make good free of charge to Buyer any loss of or damage to or defect in the goods where notice is given by Buyer in compliance with this condition provided that Buyer shall not in any event claim damage in respect of loss of profits.

8 Acceptance

In the case of goods delivered by Seller not conforming with the Contract whether by reason of being of quality or in a quantity measurement not stipulated or being unfit for the purpose for which they are required where such purpose has been made known in writing to Seller, Buyer shall have the right to reject such goods within a reasonable time of their delivery and to purchase elsewhere as near as practicable to the same Contract specifications and conditions as circumstances shall permit but without prejudice to any other right which Buyer might have against Seller. The making of payment shall not prejudice Buyer's right of rejection. Before exercising the said right to purchase elsewhere Buyer shall give Seller reasonable opportunity to replace rejected goods with goods which conform to the Contract.

9 **Variations**

Seller shall not alter any of the goods, except as directed in writing by Buyer; but Buyer shall have the right, from time to time during the execution of the Contract, by notice in writing to direct Seller to add to or omit, or otherwise vary, the goods, and Seller shall carry out such variations and be bound by the same conditions, so far as applicable, as though the said variations were stated in the Contract.

Where Seller receives any such direction from Buyer which would occasion an amendment to the Contract Price, Seller shall, with all possible speed, advise Buyer in writing to that effect giving the amount of any such amendment, ascertained and determined at the same level of pricing as that contained in Seller's tender.

If, in the opinion of Seller, any such direction is likely to prevent Seller from fulfilling any of his obligations under the Contract he shall so notify Buyer and Buyer shall decide with all possible speed whether or not the same shall be carried out and shall confirm his instructions in writing and modify the said obligations to such an extent as may be justified. Until Buyer so confirms his instructions they shall be deemed not to have been given.

10 **Intellectual property rights**

10.1 Seller will indemnify Buyer against any claim for infringement of patents, designs or registered designs, trade mark or copyright by the use or sale of any article or material supplied by Seller to Buyer and against all costs and damages (including legal fees) which the Buyer may incur in any action for such infringement or for which Buyer may become liable in such action. Provided always that this indemnity shall not apply to any infringement which is due to Seller having followed a design or instruction furnished or given by Buyer or to the use of such article or material in a manner or for a purpose or in a foreign country not specified by or disclosed to Seller, or to any infringement which is due to the use of such article or material in association or combination with any other article or material not supplied by Seller. Provided also that this indemnity is conditional on Buyer giving to Seller the earliest possible notice in writing of any claim being made or action threatened or brought against Buyer.

10.2 All intellectual property rights in works, goods or materials produced for buyer by Seller or specifically commissioned by Seller from Buyer shall vest in Buyer and Seller undertakes to execute all documents required to ensure such ownership.

11 **Force majeure**

Neither party shall be liable for failure to perform its obligations under the Contract if such failure results from circumstances which could not have been contemplated and which are beyond the party's reasonable control. Force majeure does not include strikes or industrial disputes or failures of sub-contractors.

12 **Progress and inspection**
Buyer's representatives shall have the right to progress and inspect all goods at Seller's works and the works of sub-contractors at all reasonable times and to reject goods that do not comply with the terms of the Contract. Seller's sub-contracts shall include this provision. Any inspection, checking, approval or acceptance given on behalf of Buyer shall not relieve Seller or his sub-contractors from any obligation under the Contract.

13 **Buyer's rights in specifications, plans, drawings, patterns, etc.**
Any specifications, plans, drawings, patterns or designs supplied by Buyer to Seller in connection with the Contract shall remain the property of Buyer, and any information derived therefrom or otherwise communicated to Seller in connection with the Contract shall be regarded by Seller as secret and confidential and shall not, without the consent in writing of Buyer, be published or disclosed to any third party, or made use of by Seller except for the purpose of implementing the Contract.

14 **Responsibility for information**
Seller shall be responsible for any errors or omissions in any drawings, calculations, packing details or other particulars supplied by him, whether such information has been approved by Buyer or not, provided that such errors or omissions are not due to inaccurate information furnished in writing by Buyer.

15 **Assignment and sub-letting**
The Contract shall not be assigned by Seller nor sub-let as a whole. Seller shall not sub-let any part of the work without Buyer's written consent, but the restriction contained in this clause shall not apply to sub-contracts for materials, for minor details, or for any part of which the makers are named in the Contract. Seller shall be responsible for all work done and goods supplied by all sub-contractors.

16 **Copies of sub-orders**
When Buyer has consented to the placing of sub-contracts copies of each sub-order shall be sent by Seller to Buyer immediately it is issued.

17 **Deterioration**
Except where stated otherwise in Buyer's Purchase Order, Seller shall protect any item or part that might deteriorate during transportation or storage.

18 **Free-issue materials**
Where Buyer for the purposes of the Contract issues materials free of charge to Seller such materials shall be and remain the property of Buyer. Seller shall

maintain all such materials in good order and condition subject, in the case of tooling, patterns and the like, to fair wear and tear. Seller shall use such material solely in connection with the Contract. Any surplus materials shall be disposed of at Buyer's discretion. Waste of such materials arising from bad workmanship or negligence of Seller shall be made good at Seller's expense. Without prejudice to any other of the rights of the Buyer, Seller shall deliver up such materials whether further processed or not to Buyer on demand.

19 **Warranty**
Seller shall as soon as reasonably practicable repair or replace all goods which are or become defective during the period of 12 months from putting into service or 18 months from delivery, whichever shall be the shorter, where such defects occur under proper usage and are due to faulty design, Seller's erroneous instructions as to use or erroneous use data, or inadequate or faulty materials or workmanship, or any other breach of Seller's warranties, express or implied. Repairs and replacements shall themselves be subject to the foregoing obligations for a period of 12 months from the date of delivery, reinstallation or passing of tests (if any) whichever is appropriate after repair or replacement. Seller shall further be liable in damages (if any) in respect of each Purchase Order provided that such damages and losses were reasonably foreseeable.

20 **Insolvency and bankruptcy**
If Seller becomes insolvent or bankrupt or (being a Company) makes an arrangement with its creditors or has an administrative receiver or administrator appointed or commences to be wound up (other than for the purposes of amalgamation or reconstruction), Buyer may, without prejudice to any other of his rights, terminate the Contract forthwith by notice to Seller or any person in whom the Contract may have become vested.

21 **General conditions in the tender**
No conditions submitted or referred to by Seller when tendering shall form part of the Contract unless otherwise agreed to in writing by Buyer.

22 **Applicable law and jurisdiction**
This contract shall be subject to English law and the parties submit to the exclusive jurisdiction of the English Courts.

23 **Notices**
Any notice to be sent under this Agreement should be sent to the addresses given on page one and served personally or by pre-paid registered or recorded delivery letter or fax confirmed by first class post. Letters shall be deemed served 48 hours after posting and fax on despatch.

24 **Waiver**
No delay or omission by Buyer in exercising any of its rights or remedies under

this Agreement or under any applicable law on any occasion shall be deemed a waiver of, or bar to, the exercise of such right or remedy or any other right or remedy upon any other occasion.

25 Headings
The headings in this Agreement are for ease of reference only and shall not affect the construction thereof.

26 Severance
In the event that any provision of this Agreement shall be void or unenforceable by reason of any provision or applicable law, it shall be deleted and the remaining provisions hereof shall continue in full force and effect and, if necessary, be so amended as shall be necessary to give effect to the spirit of the Agreement so far as possible.

Guidance notes on the use of Model Two:

'Conditions of Contract for Engineering Plant and Materials
(Inclusive of Erection or Supervision of Erection)'

1 **Use**

Use when it is considered beneficial to employ the Seller's expertise during the **erection** phases of engineering equipment, eg

1.1 For all **supply, deliver, erect** orders where the site work cost is only a small proportion of the total price and involves only a few men on site for a short time for each piece of equipment supplied, ie

Major machines such as compressors, large motors, etc.

Transformers

Switchgear and control gear

Pumps and other special-purpose machinery.

1.2 For all **supply, deliver, supervise erection** orders.

2 **General note on negotiation**

Always specify in the enquiry that it is a condition of the order that these Conditions are to be accepted. If the Seller raises any objections these can then be the basis for negotiation. Avoid attempting to amend the Seller's conditions to meet the Buyer's requirements (see Part One, Section 1.4).

3 **Definition of requirements**

The following information should be part of any enquiry and/or purchase order.

3.1 Quantity.

3.2 Comprehensive specification of all matters affecting the design, operating conditions, performance, duty, climatic conditions, limits of utilities, etc. (see note 4.4).

3.3 Date by which completion is required; be specific (see Part One, Section 5 Seller's Default).

3.4 Delivery point. This is particularly important from the point of view of establishing the point of passing of property and risk (see note 4.3).

3.5 Terms of payment, including retention money (if any) (see note 4).

3.6 Whether price is fixed or subject to a price-adjustment formula (see note 4.1).

3.7 Liquidated damages (if any) (see Part One, Section 5.2).

3.8 Whether subject to the Buyer's inspection and expediting.

3.9 State what utilities and other facilities (e.g. accommodation, welfare etc.) will be provided by the Buyer.

3.10 Define the Seller's site responsibilitites (see note 4.2)

3.11 Specify who is responsible for off-loading and storage and what notice and arrangements are required for acceptance of delivery.

3.12 Fabrication, erection and commissioning programme as necessary including dates when design and detail information and any 'free-issue' items must be available.

3.13 Performance tests, procedure for acceptance and guarantees (see note 4.13).

3.14 Stipulate any restrictions to be imposed on sub-letting (see note 4.8).

3.15 State any special or unusual requirements and any special markings required on materials or equipment (see note 4.4).

3.16 Specify any material which is to be of 'free-issue' (see note 4.7).

3.17 Specify any special protection, packing or transport requirements.

4 Notes on certain clauses

4.1 Clause 3 − 'Terms of payment' (see Part One, Section 4):
The terms of payment *must* be specified on the order, including retention money (if any). Usually the basis will be one of the following:

1 an 'all-in' fixed price

2 an 'all-in' price subject to a price-adjustment formula

3 a price for equipment with separate rates for site work/attendance

4 stage payments

4.1.1 Relate time of payment to date of take-over of the equipment by the Buyer. It is recommended that some money (retention money) should be retained until the end of the warranty period as 'insurance' against the Seller not fulfilling his obligations under the contract, e.g. performance tests, warranty, etc.

4.1.2   Where stage payments have to be agreed these should be related to, and conditional upon, work done. See also reference to stage payments in note 4.4.2.

4.1.3   Although it is the recommended practice to obtain a 'fixed price', it may be more economical in the case of high-value, extended-delivery items to agree a price subject to a price-adjustment formula. This may work out cheaper than a 'pre-loaded' firm price. In such cases the BEAMA CPA System is recommended (see Part One, Section 4.7).

4.2   Clause 4 − 'Inclusions in price':
To avoid complications at a later stage it is recommended that the enquiry includes an instruction to the Seller to visit the site and discuss all aspects of the contract. Remember to specify the person to whom the Seller should report.

4.3   Clause 7 − 'Passing of property':

4.3.1   Where the Seller is responsible for erection, regardless of where the equipment is manufactured, it is advisable to make him responsible for delivery to the required site. Responsibility for off-loading should be agreed prior to delivery.

4.3.2   Where the Buyer is responsible for erection the Seller should be made responsible for delivery to the required site. The Buyer would generally be responsible for off-loading.

4.4   Clause 9 − 'Rejection':

4.4.1   It is advisable to specify in detail in the contract documents the purposes for which the equipment is required and the varying conditions under which it will operate. This is particularly important in respect of any rights of rejection.

4.4.2   This clause provides for the Buyer to reject any equipment or work done on the site from the time of delivery up to the time when the equipment is ready for testing. The right of rejection remains with the Buyer even though agreed stage payments may have been made.

4.4.3   When the equipment is ready for testing however, the provisions of Clause 26 apply (see note 4.13).

4.5 Clause 10 – 'Intellectual property rights':
This clause must *not* be altered in any way without legal guidance.

4.6 Clause 11 –'Force majeure': (see Part One, Section 5.5):

4.6.1 The Buyer should only pay an equitable sum in respect of cancellation charges, taking account of the loss that may be incurred by both parties and the degree to which such losses are insurable. The Seller should be covered by insurance in respect of consequential losses, e.g. loss of profits, loss of other contracts, interruption of business, etc., and fire or explosion at the Seller's works. Negotiations should therefore be restricted to costs in respect of materials and labour actually expended up to the date of cancellation.

4.6.2 With regard to the imposition of supply by allocation due to force majeure circumstances every endeavour should be made by the Buyer to obtain an assurance from the Seller that all his customers are allocated goods on an equal basis. If any of the goods are being manufactured or processed by the Seller – whether for his own use or for sale – albeit at a reduced rate due to force majeure, the imposition of allocations is not itself covered by the definition of force majeure since the choice of customer/user *is* under the Seller's control and at his own discretion.

4.6.3 The Seller is not entitled to impose any additional charges in respect of the storage of goods during a force majeure situation unless there is provision for such extra charges in the terms of the contract.

4.6.4 Remember, a delivery extension granted under a force majeure situation also extends the period before which liquidated damages (if any) are payable.

4.7 Clause 16 – 'Free-issue materials':
Where the order provides for a significant amount of free-issue materials consideration should be given to the use of the Special Conditions detailed in Part One, Section 7.2, to protect the Buyer and allow him to retrieve his materials should the Seller find himself in financial difficulties.

4.8 Clause 18 – 'Assignment and sub-letting':
If it is anticipated that the Seller intends to sub-let a significant part of the work then the details must be discussed and agreed with the Seller before the order is placed.

4.9 Clause 19 — 'Variations':
Whilst the Seller has the right to propose changes to the specification the Conditions make it necessary for the Buyer to confirm the variation.

4.10 Clause 20 — 'Site work by Seller':
The information required under 20.1 and 20.2 should be discussed and agreed with the Seller before the order is placed.

4.11 Clauses 22 and 23 —'Indemnity and insurance':
These clauses set out proposed wording to safeguard the Buyer but guidance should be sought from one's own broker regarding the value and extent of the cover required from the Seller. However, make sure that Clause 23.2 is put into effect.

4.12 Clause 25 — 'Loan of Buyer's plant and equipment':
Any plant and equipment on hire to the Buyer from a third party must *not* be loaned to the Seller as this may invalidate the hire agreement and put the Buyer at risk. No insurance cover is available for any loss or damage that could occur whilst such plant is being used by the Seller.

4.13 Clause 26 — 'Completion tests and take-over':
This clause sets out the ground rules for conducting the completion tests. Sub-clause 26.3 has provisions for tests being delayed by the Buyer, e.g. shortage of feedstock, delays by other contractors etc., and sub-clause 26.6 sets out the remedies available to the Buyer should the equipment fail to meet the required tests.

4.14 Clause 27 — 'Warranty period':
This clause defines the Seller's liabilities after take-over. The total claim by the Buyer is limited to the restoration of the equipment to full working order, plus reimbursement of any reasonably foreseeable losses.

4.15 Clause 29 — 'Insolvency and bankruptcy':
This clause reflects the Insolvency Act 1985 which introduces the 'administrator' and 'administrative receiver'. Among the reasons why an administrator might be appointed are:

1 to continue the company in whole or in part

2 to optimise assets for liquidation.

5 Overseas application
These model conditions may be adapted for use with overseas sources of supply by reference to Part One, Section 9

Model Two

Conditions of Contract for Engineering Plant and Materials
(Inclusive of Erection or Supervision of Erection)

1 **Definitions**

   1.1   The term 'Buyer' shall mean the person, firm or company so named in the Purchase Order.

   1.2   The term 'Seller' shall mean the person, firm or company to whom the Purchase Order is issued.

   1.3   'The Equipment' shall mean all machinery, apparatus, materials and articles to be supplied by Seller and/or his sub-contractors and forming a permanent part of the Work.

   1.4   'The Work' shall mean the supply, delivery, erection or supervision of erection and/or commissioning of the Equipment as detailed in the Contract.

   1.5   'The Site' shall mean the location where the Work is to be performed.

   1.6   The term 'Purchase Order' shall mean Buyer's Purchase Order which specifies that these conditions apply to it.

   1.7   'The Contract' shall mean the contract between the Buyer and Seller consisting of the Purchase Order, these conditions and any other documents (or parts thereof) specified in the Purchase Order. Should there be any inconsistency between the documents comprising the contract, they shall have precedence in the order herein listed.

2 **Completion date**

The date of completion of the Work shall be that specified in the Purchase Order unless agreed otherwise between Buyer and Seller. Seller shall furnish such programmes of manufacture and delivery as Buyer may reasonably require and Seller shall give notice to Buyer as soon as practicable if such programmes are, or are likely to be, delayed.

If the Work includes tests the same shall not be deemed to be completed until such tests have been passed to the reasonable satisfaction of Buyer.

3 Terms of payment

Unless otherwise stated in the Contract, payment will be made within 28 days of receipt and agreement of invoices submitted following Take-Over of the Work in accordance with clause 26.

4 Inclusions in price

4.1 Seller is deemed to have understood the nature and extent of the Work and to have visited the Site and shall make no claim founded on his failure to do so. Buyer shall, on request of Seller, grant such access as may be reasonable for this purpose.

4.2 Unless otherwise specified, the Seller shall provide all plant, tools, material, labour, haulage and other things necessary to complete the Works.

4.3 Seller shall complete the Work in accordance with all statutory obligations that apply and with the instructions and programme as set out in the Contract.

5 General conditions in the tender

No conditions submitted or referred to by Seller when tendering shall form part of the Contract unless otherwise agreed to in writing by Buyer.

6 Incorrect delivery

All Equipment must be delivered at the delivery point specified in the Purchase Order. If any Equipment is incorrectly delivered Seller shall be responsible for any additional expense incurred in delivering it to the correct delivery point.

7 Passing of property to buyer

The property in the Equipment shall remain in Seller until it is delivered at the said delivery point.

8 Deterioration

Seller shall protect any item or part that might deteriorate during transportation or storage.

9 Rejection

If at any time before the Work is taken over under Clause 26 (Completion Tests and Take-Over) Buyer shall:

1   decide that any of the Equipment or Work is not in accordance with the Contract or is otherwise defective (all such matters being hereinafter in this clause called 'defects'), and

2   as soon as reasonably practicable give to Seller notice in writing of the said decision specifying particulars of the defects alleged and of where the same are alleged to exist or to have occurred, and

3   so far as may be necessary place the Equipment or Work at Seller's disposal, then Seller shall at his own expense and with all speed make good the defects so specified. In case Seller shall fail so to do Buyer may, provided he does so without undue delay, take, at the cost of Seller, such steps as may in all the circumstances be reasonable to make good such defects. All equipment provided by Buyer to replace defective Equipment shall comply with the Contract and shall be obtained where reasonably practicable under competitive conditions. Seller shall be entitled to remove and retain all Equipment that Buyer may have replaced at Seller's cost. The making of any payment shall not prejudice the Buyer's right of rejection hereunder.

10 Intellectual property rights

10.1   Seller will indemnify Buyer against any claim for infringement of patents, registered designs and designs, trade mark or copyright by the Work or by the use or sale of the Equipment and against all costs and damages which Buyer may incur in any action for such infringement or for which Buyer may become liable in any such action. Provided always that this indemnity shall not apply to any infringement which is due to Seller having followed a design or instruction furnished or given by Buyer or to the use of such Equipment in a manner or for a purpose or in a country (other than the United Kingdom) not specified by or disclosed to Seller, or to any infringement which is due to the use of such Equipment in association or combination with any other equipment not supplied by Seller. Provided also that this indemnity is conditional on Buyer giving to Seller the earliest possible notice in writing of any claim being made or action threatened or brought against Buyer.

10.2   All intellectual property rights in works, goods or materials produced for Buyer by Seller or specifically commissioned by Seller from Buyer shall vest in Buyer and Seller undertakes to execute all documents required to ensure such ownership.

11 Force majeure
Neither party shall be liable for failure to perform its obligations under the Contract if such failure results from circumstances which could not have been contemplated and which are beyond the party's reasonable control. Force majeure does not include strikes or industrial disputes or failure of sub-contractors.

12 Progress and inspection
Buyer's representatives shall have the right to progress and inspect the Equipment at Seller's works and the works of Seller's sub-contractors at all reasonable times and to reject any part thereof that does not comply with the terms of the Contract. Seller's sub-contracts shall be made accordingly. Any inspection, checking, approval or acceptance given on behalf of Buyer shall not relieve Seller or his

sub-contractors from any obligation under the Contract.

13 Buyer's rights in specifications, plans, drawings, patterns, etc.

Any specifications, plans, drawings, patterns or designs supplied by Buyer to Seller in connection with the Contract shall remain the property of Buyer, and any information derived therefrom or otherwise communicated to Seller in connection with the Contract shall be held by Seller as secret and confidential and shall not, without the consent in writing of Buyer, be published or disclosed to any third party, or made use of by Seller except for the purpose of implementing the Contract.

14 Responsibility for information

Seller shall be responsible for any errors or omissions in any drawings, calculations, packing details or other particulars supplied by him, whether such information has been approved by Buyer or not, provided that such errors or omissions are not due to inaccurate information furnished in writing by Buyer.

15 Things found on the Site

All minerals, metals, objects and other things found or discovered on, under or around the Site shall as between the Contractor and the Buyer be the property of the Buyer and shall be dealt with as the Buyer may direct.

16 Free-issue materials

Where Buyer for the purpose of the Contract issues materials 'free of charge' to Seller such materials shall be and remain the property of Buyer. Seller shall maintain all such materials in good order and condition subject, in the case of tooling, patterns and the like, to fair wear and tear. Seller shall use such materials solely in connection with the Contract. Any surplus materials shall be disposed of at Buyer's discretion. Waste of such materials arising from bad workmanship or negligence of Seller shall be made good at Seller's expense. Without prejudice to any other of the rights of the Buyer, Seller shall deliver up such materials, whether further processed or not, to Buyer on demand.

17 Site regulations

17.1   Seller shall make no delivery nor commence work on Site before obtaining the consent of Buyer.

17.2   Seller shall comply with Buyer's 'Works Rules' (available on request) and the safety requirements applicable to the Site and shall ensure that his employees so comply.

17.3   Buyer shall have the right to require the removal of any person brought to the Site by the Seller who has:

1   failed to comply with the 'Works Rules', or

2   has, in the opinion of Buyer, misconducted himself or been negligent or incompetent.

18 Assignment and sub-letting

18.1   The Contract shall not be assigned by Seller nor shall the Work be sub-let as a whole. Seller shall not sub-let any part of the Work without Buyer's written consent, but the restriction contained in this clause shall not apply to sub-contracts for materials, for minor details, or for any part of the Work of which the makers are named in the Contract. Seller shall be responsible for all Work done and Equipment supplied by all Sub-Contractors.

18.2   When Buyer has consented to the placing of sub-contracts copies of each sub-order shall be sent by Seller to Buyer immediately it is issued.

19 Variations

Seller shall not alter any of the Equipment or the Work, except as directed in writing by Buyer; but Buyer shall have the right, from time to time during the execution of the Contract, by notice in writing to direct Seller to add to or omit, or otherwise vary, the Equipment or the Work, and Seller shall carry out such variations and be bound by the same conditions, so far as applicable, as though the said variations were stated in the Contract.

Where Seller receives any such direction from Buyer which would occasion an amendment to the Contract Price Seller shall, with all possible speed, advise Buyer in writing to that effect giving the amount of any such amendment, ascertained and determined at the same level of pricing as that contained in Seller's tender.

If, in the opinion of Seller, any such direction is likely to prevent Seller from fulfilling any of his obligations under the Contract he shall so notify Buyer and Buyer shall decide with all possible speed whether or not the same shall be carried out and shall confirm his instructions in writing and modify the said obligations to such an extent as may be justified. Until Buyer so confirms his instructions they shall be deemed not to have been given.

20 Site work by seller

If any work on Site is to be carried out by Seller other than the supervision of erection and/or commissioning, then Seller shall comply with the following:

1   Before delivery is made, arrange for the off-loading and adequate storage of Equipment to be erected by him if so specified in the Contract.

2   Before employing hourly-paid workers on the Site, agree with the Buyer the hours to be worked (including overtime), basic wages, bonus and other conditions of employment. Such matters shall not be changed without Buyer's written consent except in compliance with National Agreements.

21 Secrecy

No photographs of any of Buyer's equipment, installations or property shall be taken without Buyer's prior consent in writing. Seller shall keep secret and shall not divulge to any third party (except Sub-Contractors accepting a like obligation of secrecy, and then only to the extent necessary for the performance of the sub-contract) all information given by Buyer in connection with the Contract or which becomes known to Seller through his performance of the Work under the Contract.

Seller shall not mention Buyer's name in connection with the Contract or disclose the existence of the Contract in any publicity material or other similar communication to third parties without Buyer's prior consent in writing.

22 Indemnity

Seller shall take every practicable precaution not to damage or injure any property or persons. Seller shall satisfy all claims founded on any such damage or injury which arise out of or in consequence of any operations under the Contract whether such claims are made by Buyer or by a third party against Seller or against Buyer, and Seller shall indemnify Buyer against all actions, demands, damages, costs, charges and expenses (including legal fees) arising in connection therewith provided, however, that nothing in this condition shall render Seller liable for any injury or damage resulting from any negligent act or omission of Buyer, his servants or agents, or any other contractor employed by Buyer and Buyer shall indemnify Seller against all demands and expenses arising in connection with any such damage or injury.

23 Insurance

23.1 Seller shall have in force and shall require any Sub-Contractor to have in force:

(a) Employer's Liability Insurance and

(b) Public Liability Insurance for such sum and range of cover as Seller deems to be appropriate but not less than £1,000,000 for any one accident unless otherwise agreed by the Buyer in writing.

All such insurances shall be extended to indemnify Buyer against any claim for which Seller or any Sub-Contractor may be legally liable.

23.2 The Policy of Insurance shall be shown to Buyer whenever he requests, together with satisfactory evidence of payment premiums.

23.3 Buyer shall maintain Employer's Liability and Public Liability Insurance in respect of his own liabilities.

24 Notification procedure

24.1 Seller shall give advance notice of any performance test or plant start-up to be carried out solely by Seller or his Sub-Contractor after the Date of Taking Over (see Clause 26).

24.2 Seller shall give immediate notice in the event of any accident or damage likely to form the subject of a claim under Buyer's insurance and shall give all the information and assistance in respect thereof that Buyer's insurers may require, and shall not negotiate, pay, settle, admit or repudiate any claim without their written consent, and shall permit the insurers to take proceedings in the name of Seller to recover compensation or secure an indemnity from any third party in respect of any of the matters covered by the said insurance.

25 Loan of buyer's plant and equipment
(The inclusion of this condition does not imply that Buyer assumes any obligations to provide 'Loaned Plant' which means plant or equipment owned by Buyer and used by or on behalf of Seller by agreement.)

25.1 Where Loaned Plant is operated by a servant of Buyer:

(a) The Operator shall not become the servant of Seller but carry out with the Loaned Plant such work as he may be directed to do by Seller.

(b) Seller shall be liable for any damage to the Loaned Plant caused by misdirection or misuse of it due to negligence on the part of Seller, his servants or agents.

(c) Buyer shall be liable for any damage to the Loaned Plant caused by a defect in or faulty operation of the Plant.

25.2 Where Loaned Plant is operated by a servant of Seller or an independent Contractor, Seller shall be liable for all damage to the Loaned Plant unless he can show that it was caused by a defect in the plant at the commencement of the loan and he shall be liable for any loss (including loss by theft) of the said plant.

25.3 Buyer shall have the right to withdraw Loaned Plant at any time and shall be under no liability whatever in connection with Buyer failing to lend plant at any time.

25.4 Seller shall satisfy himself that any Loaned Plant is suitable for the purpose intended.

26 Completion tests and take-over

26.1 Completion tests, which shall be in accordance with the provision of the Contract, shall be made at a time to be agreed with Buyer. Seller shall give Buyer 14 days' notice of the date after which he will be ready to carry out the tests. Subject to the provisions of paragraph 26.3, if Buyer fails to attend at the time agreed Seller shall be entitled to proceed in his absence and the tests shall be deemed to have been made in the presence of Buyer.

26.2 When the erection of the Equipment is complete and all tests to be made by Seller have been passed to the reasonable satisfaction of Buyer, Buyer shall forthwith take-over the Equipment and shall certify accordingly.

26.3 If by reason of difficulties encountered by Buyer it becomes impossible to proceed with the said tests, these shall be postponed for a period not exceeding 3 months, or such other period as may be agreed, and the following shall apply:

(a) Buyer shall make payment as if Take-Over had taken place, provided that in the case of a difficulty due to any circumstances falling within the provisions of Clause 11 *(Force Majeure)* Buyer shall not be required to pay at the due time of Take-Over the cost of uncompleted work.

(b) At the earliest possible time during the said agreed period of postponement Buyer shall give notice in writing to Seller stating the earliest date on which the said tests can be carried out and requesting him to conduct the test within 10 days of the date mentioned in such notice.

(c) The Warranty Period shall run from the date when the tests have been successfully carried out or, in the event that the tests are carried out after the agreed period of postponement, from the date of the written notice given in accordance with 26.3(d).

(d) If at the end of the period of postponement the said tests have not taken place the Work shall be deemed to have been completed and the Warrany Period shall commence on written notice to that effect being given by Seller to Buyer.

(e) Seller may, at the cost of Buyer, examine the Equipment and make good any defect or deterioration therein that may have developed, or loss thereof that may have occurred, after the date when the Work was first postponed.

(f) All reasonable expenses incurred by Seller by reason of the postponement of the Work by Buyer (otherwise than in consequence of some default on the part of Seller) shall be paid by Buyer, provided that no claim shall be made under this clause unless Seller has, within a reasonable time, given notice in writing to Buyer of his intention to make such claim.

26.4 Buyer may take-over any part of the Equipment whether or not it has passed all its tests and shall certify accordingly in respect of that part.

26.5 Buyer shall be responsible for the care and operation of any part of the Equipment certified as taken-over.

26.6 In the event of the Equipment or any part of it failing to meet the tests specified in the Contract, Buyer will notify Seller accordingly. Seller shall take all reasonable action forthwith to rectify the same but in the event of continuing failure of the Equipment to meet the specified tests Buyer may:

(a) assist in the rectification at Seller's expense or,

(b) take over the Equipment conditional upon Seller accepting a reduction in the Contract Price, or

(c) reject the Equipment and in such event Seller shall refund any moneys paid by Buyer in respect of the Equipment concerned (including the appropriate proportion of erection charges where applicable) and shall pay or allow to Buyer any sum by which the expenditure reasonably incurred by Buyer in replacing the rejected Equipment, including the cost of the replacement equipment and all labour, materials and other expenses incidental to such replacement, exceeds the amount of the moneys refunded. Such right of rejection shall remain available to Buyer even though assistance has been rendered under 26.6(a). Seller shall be entitled to remove and retain all items that Buyer may have replaced at Seller's cost.

27 **Warranty period**
Seller shall as soon as reasonably practicable repair or replace any part of the Equipment or the Work which is or becomes defective during the period of 12 months from date of Take-Over by Buyer, where such defects occur under proper usage and are due to faulty design (other than a design made, furnished, or specified by Buyer for which Seller has disclaimed responsibility in writing), Seller's erroneous instructions or workmanship, or any other breach of Seller's warranties, express or implied. Repairs and replacements shall themselves be subject to the foregoing obligations for a period of 12 months from the date of reinstallation or passing of tests (if any) whichever is appropriate after repair or replacement. Seller shall further be liable in damages for all reasonably foreseeable losses.

In the event that Seller cannot respond within a reasonable time to rectify a defect as defined above Buyer may carry out the repair or replacement and shall be entitled to reimbursement by Seller for such costs as would have been incurred by Seller's normal methods. Such action shall not relieve Seller of his continuing obligations under the Contract.

28   Seller's default

28.1   If Seller fails to carry out promptly any of Buyer's instructions, and fails within 10 days of notice by Buyer drawing attention to such failure to take such steps as reasonably satisfy Buyer, Buyer may, without prejudice to any other of his rights, carry out the Work at the risk and expense of Seller.

28.2   If Seller commits a breach of the Contract and fails within 10 days of notice by Buyer to take such steps as reasonably satisfy Buyer to rectify such breach, Buyer may, without prejudice to any other of his rights, terminate the Contract forthwith by notice to Seller. Thereupon, without prejudice to any other of his rights, Buyer may himself complete the Work or have it completed by a third party, and Buyer shall not be liable to make any further payment to Seller until the Work has been completed in accordance with the requirements of the Contract, and shall be entitled to deduct from the Contract Price any additional cost incurred by Buyer. If the total cost to Buyer exceeds the Contract Price, the difference shall be recoverable by Buyer from Seller.

29   Insolvency and bankruptcy
If Seller becomes insolvent or bankrupt or (being a Company) makes an arrangement with its creditors or has an administrative receiver or administrator appointed or commences to be wound up (other than for the purposes of amalgamation or reconstruction), Buyer may, without prejudice to any other of his rights, terminate the Contract forthwith by notice to Seller or any person in whom the Contract may have become vested.

30   Applicable law and jurisdiction
This contract shall be subject to English law and the parties submit to the exclusive jurisdiction of the English Courts.

31   Notices
Any notice to be sent under this Agreement should be sent to the addresses given on page one and served personally or by pre-paid registered or recorded delivery letter or fax confirmed by first class post. Letters shall be deemed served 48 hours after posting and fax on despatch.

32   Waiver
No delay or omission by Buyer in exercising any of its rights or remedies under

this Agreement or under any applicable law on any occasion shall be deemed a waiver of, or bar to, the exercise of such right or remedy or any other right or remedy upon any other occasion.

33. Headings

The headings in this Agreement are for ease of reference only and shall not affect the construction thereof.

34. Severance

In the event that any provision of this Agreement shall be void or unenforceable by reason of any provision or applicable law, it shall be deleted and the remaining provisions hereof shall continue in full force and effect and, if necessary, be so amended as shall be necessary to give effect to the spirit of the Agreement so far as possible.

Guidance notes on the use of Model Three:

'General Conditions of Contract (for other than Engineering Goods)'

1 Use

Use for the **supply and delivery** of raw materials (whether in solid, powder, liquid or gaseous form), packaging materials, office furniture and stationery, and all similar non-engineering goods.

2 General note on negotiation

Always specify in the enquiry that it is a condition of the order that these Conditions are to be accepted. If the Seller raises any objections these can then be the basis for negotiation. Avoid attempting to amend Seller's conditions to meet the Buyer's requirements (see Part One, Section 1, pages 13-15).

3 Definition of requirements

The following information should be part of any enquiry and/or purchase order:

3.1   Quantity, description and specification (eg British, European, or International, drawing number etc) of goods. Are samples required?

3.2   Delivery date(s); be specific (see Part One Section 5 – Seller's Default).

3.3   Delivery point.

3.4   Terms of payment (see note 4.3).

3.5   Whether price is fixed or subject to a price-adjustment formula (see note 4.3).

3.6   Liquidated damages (if any) (see Part One, Section 5, page 28-29).

3.7   Whether subject to the Buyer's inspection and expediting.

3.8   Delivery programme, where deliveries are phased to production, and dates when any 'free-issue' iems will be available.

3.9   Specify any material which is to be of 'free-issue' (see note 4.7).

3.10   Stipulate any restrictions to be imposed on sub-letting (see note 4.6).

3.11   Any special protection, packing or transport requirements.

4   **Notes on certain clauses**

4.1   Clauses 2 and 8 − 'Quality' and 'Acceptance':
It is advisable to specify in detail the materials and the purpose for which the goods are required, eg in the case of a chemical substance, the degree of purity; for moulding powders the temperature and flow characteristics.

4.2   Clause 5 − 'Passing of property and risk to Buyer':
Make the Seller responsible for delivery to the required site; and 'ex works' offer should not normally be agreed. In the latter case property and risk pass to the Buyer when the goods are loaded on transport at the Seller's works. The Buyer will not only have to pay for transport but may also find it necessary to arrange special insurance cover against damage or loss in transit. See the provisions of Part One, Section 4, page 24 et seq., with regard to the relationship between the passing of property and stage payments.

4.3   Clause 6 − 'Terms of payment' (see Part One, Section 4, page 22 et seq.)

   (a)   The terms of payment given are generally acceptable to most suppliers. Where different terms are negotiated for specific orders or with particular suppliers such terms must be stated on the Purchase Order.

   (b)   Although it is recommended practice to obtain a 'fixed price', it may be more economical in the case of long-term contracts to agree to a price subject to a price-adjustment formula. This may work out cheaper than a 'pre-loaded' firm price. When considering price-adjustment formulae it is advisable to opt for a nationally recognised system (see Part One, Section 4, page 24).

4.4   Clause 7 − 'Loss or damage in transit'
It is usual for the Seller to require notification or loss or damage in such a manner as to comply with the carrier's conditions. However, the Buyer is not party to the contract between the Seller and the carrier and cannot therefore reasonably be deemed to know of, or to have accepted, the terms of that contract. The model clause should be acceptable to the majority of suppliers.

4.5   Clause 11 − 'Force majeure' (see Part One, Section 5.5)

   (a)   Costs should lie where they fall in the case of cancellation due to force majeure. The Buyer should not pay cancellation charges. The Seller should be covered by insurance in respect of consequential losses, eg loss of profits, loss of other contracts, interruption of business, etc. and fire or explosion at Seller's works. Negotiations should therefore be restricted to costs in respect of materials and labour actually expended up to the date of cancellation.

(b) The Seller is not entitled to impose any additional charges in respect of the storage of goods during a force majeure situation unless there is provision for such extra charges in the terms of the contract.

(c) Remember, a delivery extension granted under a force majeure situation also extends the period before which liquidated damages (if any) are payable.

(d) With regard to the imposition of supply by allocation because of force majeure circumstance every endeavour should be made by the Buyer to obtain an assurance from the Seller that all his customers are allocated goods on an equal basis. If any of the goods are being manufactured or processed by the Seller — whether for his own use or for sale — albeit at a reduced rate due to force majeure, the imposition of allocations is not itself covered by the definition of force majeure since the choice of customer/user *is* under the Seller's contol and at his own discretion.

(e) Where a price is established relative to a given quantity, no variation in that price basis should be allowed if the Buyer is forced to take a reduced quantity due to a declaration of force majeure.

4.6   Clause 12 — 'Assignment and sub-letting':
If it is anticipated that the Seller intends to sub-let a significant part of the order then the details must be discussed and agreed with the Seller before the order is placed.

4.7   Clause 16 — 'Free-issue materials':
Where the order provides for a significant amount of free-issue materials consideration should be given to the use of the Special Conditions detailed in Part One Section 7, pages 36-37, to protect the Buyer and allow him to retrieve his material, should Seller find himself in financial difficulties.

4.8   Clause 17 — 'Control of substances hazardous to health'
The Control of Substances Hazardous to Health (COSHH) Regulations 1988, made under the Health and Safety at Work Act 1974, came into force in October 1989. They provide a legal framework for the control of substances hazardous to health in all types of business, including factories, farms, quarries, leisure and service activities, offices and shops. The Regulations require employers to make an assessment of all work which is liable to expose any employee to hazardous solids, liquids, dusts,

fumes, vapours, gases or micro-organisms. The assessment must include an evaluation of the risks to health and decisions on the action needed to remove or reduce those risks.

Guidance on the type of assessment to be made in relation to particular goods or services, and the method of undertaking the assessment can be obtained by consulting the relevant Health and Safety Executive publications, available from the local office of the HSE.

Failure to comply with the requirements of the regulations can be a criminal offence, and is subject to penalties under the Health and Safety at Work etc. Act 1974. Buyers will wish to ensure therefore that, where it is the Seller's responsibility to do so, all necessary action has been taken in relation to the requirements of the regulations, including the provision of Hazard Data Sheets where these are necessary. The clause as drafted is intended as a model clause, and can be amended as appropriate to the particular circumstances.

Draft Model Clause
Hazardous Goods and Dangerous Substances

Seller shall be responsible for complying with the requirements of COSHH Regulations 1988, and any re-enactment or variation thereof and all other relevant UK and international agreements relating to the packaging, labelling and carriage of hazardous goods, including relevant statutory regulations and codes of practice.

As soon as possible following the agreement of the contract terms all information held or reasonably available to seller regarding any potential hazards known or believed to exist in the transport, handling or use of the materials supplied shall be promptly communicated to the Buyer.

4.9   Clause 18 – 'Packages':
The use of this clause will generally only be applicable where packages are chargeable unless returned (18.1 and 18.2), or goods are delivered in road/rail tankers (18.3). In such cases these terms would be acceptable to the majority of Sellers, however the Buyer could expect to negotiate terms with regard to delay in emptying rail tankers (ie demurrage).

4.10   Clause 19 – 'Warranty': See Part One, Section 1, page 20)

(a) This clause defines liabilities.

(b) Practicalities to be considered and agreed are:

– Who pays for the return of the defective goods to Seller?
– What is an acceptable time to be allowed for repair or replacement of goods?

- If service call required, are all costs covered by Warranty, ie callout, parts and labour?
- Can service be called for out of normal working hours, ie during the night, weekends and Bank Holidays?
- Is a maintenance contract (to follow the warranty period) being contemplated? – negotiate before placing the procurement contract.

4.11 Clause 20 – 'Insolvency and bankruptcy':
This clause reflects the Insolvency Act 1985 which introduced 'administrative receiver' and the 'administrator' appointed by a Court. Among the reasons why an administrator might be appointed are:

(a) to continue the company in whole or in part

(b) to optimise assets for liquidation.

5 Overseas application
These model conditions may be adapted for use with overseas sources of supply by reference to Part One, Section 9, page 48 *et seq.*

Model Three

General Conditions of Contract (for other than Engineering Goods)

1 Definitions

1.1 The term 'Buyer' shall mean the person, firm or company so named in the Purchase Order.

1.2 The term 'Seller' shall mean the person, firm or company to whom the Purchase Order is issued.

1.3 The word 'Goods' includes all goods covered by the Purchase Order whether raw materials, processed materials or fabricated products.

1.4 The word 'Packages' includes bags, cases, carboys, cylinders, drums, pallets, tank wagons and other containers.

1.5 The term 'Purchase Order' shall mean Buyer's Purchase Order which specifies that these conditions apply to it.

1.6 'The Contract' shall mean the contract between Buyer and Seller consisting of the Purchase Order, these conditions and any other documents (or parts thereof) specified in the Purchase Order. Should there be any inconsistency between the documents comprising the contract, they shall have precedence in the order herein listed.

2 Quality and fitness for purpose

The Goods shall be of satisfactory quality and free from defects in material or workmanship. If the purpose for which the Goods are required is made known to the Seller expressly or by implication the Goods shall be fit for that purpose. The Goods shall conform with the specifications, drawings, descriptions and samples contained or referred to in the Contract.

In the absence of a specification or sample, all goods supplied shall be within the normal limits of industrial quality.

3 Delivery date

The date of delivery of the Goods shall be that specified in the Purchase Order unless agreed otherwise between Buyer and Seller. Time shall be of the essence. Seller shall furnish such programmes of manufacture and delivery as Buyer may reasonably require and Seller shall give notice to Buyer as soon as practicable if such programmes are or are likely to be delayed. Buyer has the right to instruct Seller to take such action as is required to bring the Contract to completion or to reject the Goods for late delivery.

4 Incorrect delivery

All Goods must be delivered at the delivery point specified in the Purchase Order. If Goods are incorrectly delivered, Seller will be held responsible for any additional expense incurred in delivering them to their correct destination.

5 Passing of property and risk to buyer

The property and risk in the Goods shall remain in Seller until they are delivered at the point specified in the Purchase Order.

6 Terms of payment

The Purchase Order shall specify the time when invoices shall become due, and the manner in which invoices shall be submitted. Unless otherwise stated in the Purchase Order, payment will be made within 28 days of receipt of a properly prepared invoice.

Value Added Tax, where applicable, shall be shown separately on all invoices as a strictly nett extra charge.

7 Loss or damage in transit

7.1 Without prejudice to the rights of the Buyer under Clause 19 Buyer shall advise Seller and the Carrier (if any) in writing, otherwise than by a qualified signature on any Delivery Note, of any loss or damage within the following time limits:

(a) Partial loss, damage or non-delivery of any separate part of a consignment shall be advised within 7 days of date of delivery of the consignment or part consignment.

(b) Non-delivery of whole consignment shall be advised within 21 days of notice of despatch.

7.2 Seller shall make good free of charge to Buyer any loss of or damage to or defect in the Goods where notice is given by Buyer in compliance with this condition provided that Buyer shall not in any event claim damages in respect of loss of profits.

8 Acceptance

In the case of Goods delivered by Seller not conforming with the Contract whether by reason of being of quality or in a quantity measurement not stipulated or being unfit for the purpose for which they are required where such purpose has been made known in writing to Seller, Buyer shall have the right to reject such Goods within a reasonable time of their delivery and to purchase elsewhere as near as practicable to the same Contract specifications and conditions as circumstances shall permit but without prejudice to any other right which Buyer may have against Seller. The making of payment shall not prejudice Buyer's right of rejection. Before exercising the said right to purchase elsewhere Buyer shall give Seller reasonable opportunity to replace rejected Goods with Goods which conform to the contract.

9 **Variations**

Seller shall not alter any of the Goods, except as directed in writing by Buyer; but Buyer shall have the right, from time to time during the execution of the Contract, by notice in writing to direct Seller to add to or to omit, or otherwise vary, the Goods, and Seller shall carry out such variations and be bound by the same conditions, so far as applicable, as though the said variations were stated in the Contract.

Where Seller receives any such direction from Buyer which would occasion an amendment to the Contract price Seller shall, with all possible speed, advise Buyer in writing to that effect giving the amount of any such amendment, ascertained and determined at the same level of pricing as that contained in Seller's tender. The Buyer shall confirm in writing all agreed amendments to the Contract price.

If, in the opinion of Seller, any such direction is likely to prevent Seller from fulfilling any of his obligations under the Contract he shall so notify Buyer and Buyer shall decide with all possible speed whether or not the same shall be carried out and shall confirm his instructions in writing and modify the said obligations to such an extent as may be justified. Until Buyer so confirms his instructions they shall be deemed not to have been given.

10 **Intellectual property rights**

10.1 Seller will indemnify Buyer against any claim or infringement of patent, design right, registered design, trade mark or copyright by the use or sale of any article or material supplied by Seller to Buyer and against all costs and damages (including legal fees) which Buyer may incur in any action for such infringement or for which Buyer may become liable in any such action. Provided always that this indemnity shall not apply to any infringement which is due to Seller having followed any instruction furnished or given by Buyer or to the use of such article or material in a manner or for a purpose not specified by or disclosed to Seller, or to any infringement wich is due to the use of such article or material in association or combination with any other article or material not supplied by Seller. Provided also that this indemnity is conditional on Buyer giving to Seller the earliest possible notice in writing of any claim being made or action threatened or brought against Buyer.

10.2 All intellectual property rights in works, goods or materials produced for Buyer by Seller or specifically commissioned by Seller from Buyer shall vest in Buyer and Seller undertakes to execute all documents required to ensure such ownership.

11 Force majeure
Neither party shall be liable for failure to perform its obligations under the Contract if such failure results from circumstances which could not have been contemplated and which are beyond the party's reasonable control. Failure of sub-contractors and strikes are not force majeure.

12 Assignment and sub-letting
The Contract shall not be assigned by Seller nor sub-let as a whole. Seller shall not sub-let any part of the work without Buyer's written consent, but the restriction contained in this clause shall not apply to sub-contracts for materials, for minor details, or for any part of which the makers are named in the Contract. Seller shall be responsible for all work done and goods supplied by all sub-contractors.

13 Copies of sub-orders
When Buyer has consented to the placing of sub-contracts copies of each sub-order shall be sent by Seller to Buyer immediately it is issued.

14 Progress and inspection
Buyer's representatives shall have the right to progress and inspect all Goods at Seller's works and the works of sub-contractors at all reasonable times and to reject goods that do not comply with the terms of the Contract even for slight defects. Seller's sub-contracts shall include this provision. Any inspection, checking, approval or acceptance given on behalf of Buyer shall not relieve Seller or his sub-contractors from any obligation under the Contract.

15 Buyer's rights in specifications, plans, process information, etc.
Any specifications, plans, drawings, process information, patterns or designs supplied by Buyer to Seller in connection with the Contract shall remain the property of Buyer, and any information derived therefrom or otherwise communicated to Seller in connection with the Contract shall be kept secret and shall not, without the consent in writing of Buyer, be published or disclosed to any third party, or made use of by Seller except for the purpose of implementing the Contract. Any specifications, plans, drawings, process information, patterns or designs supplied by Buyer must be returned to Buyer on fulfilment of the Contract.

16 Free-issue materials
Where Buyer for the purposes of the Contract issues materials 'free of charge' to Seller such materials shall be and remain the property of Buyer. Seller shall

maintain all such materials in good order and condition subject, in the case of tooling, patterns and the like, to fair wear and tear. Seller shall use such materials solely in connection with the Contract. Any surplus materials shall be disposed of at Buyer's discretion. Waste of such materials arising from bad workmanship or negligence of Seller shall be made good at Seller's expense. Without prejudice to any other of the rights of the Buyer, Seller shall deliver up such materials whether further processed or not to the Buyer on demand.

17 Hazardous goods

17.1 Hazardous Goods must be marked by Seller with International Danger Symbol(s) and display the name of the material in English. Transport and other documents must include declaration of the hazard and name of the material in English. Goods must be accompanied by emergency information in English in the form of written instructions, labels or markings. Seller shall observe the requirements of UK and International Agreements relating to the packing, labelling and carriage of hazardous Goods.

17.2 All information held by, or reasonably available to, Seller regarding any potential hazards known or believed to exist in the transport, handling or use of the Goods supplied shall be promptly communicated to Buyer.

18 Packages

18.1 Where Buyer has an option to return Packages and does so, Buyer will return such Packages empty in good order and condition (consigned 'carriage paid' unless otherwise agreed) to Seller's supplying works or depot indicated by Seller, and will advise Seller the date of despatch.

Packages returned promptly in the manner aforesaid shall be subject to an allowance at Seller's standard rate operating at the time of delivery to Buyer.

18.2 Where Goods are delivered by road vehicle, available empty Packages may be returned by the same vehicle.

18.3 Where Goods are delivered by tank wagons these will be emptied and returned without delay.

19 Warranty

Seller shall soon as reasonably practicable repair or replace all Goods which are or become defective during the period of 12 months from putting into service or 18 months from delivery, whichever shall be the shorter, where such defects occur under proper usage and are due to faulty design, Seller's erroneous instructions as to use or erroneous use data, or inadequate or faulty materials or workmanship, or any other breach of Seller's warranties, expressed or implied.

Repairs and replacements shall themselves be subject to the foregoing obligations for a period of 12 months from the date of delivery, reinstallation or passing of tests (if any) whichever is appropriate after repair or replacement. Seller shall further be liable in damages (if any) in respect of each Purchase Order up to the limit of the price of the Goods covered by that Purchase Order.

20 **Insolvency and bankruptcy**
If Seller becomes insolvent or bankrupt or (being a Company) makes an arrangement with its creditors or has an administrative receiver or administrator appointed or commences to be wound up (other than for the purposes or amalgamation or reconstruction), Buyer may, without prejudice to any other of his rights, terminate the Contract forthwith by notice to Seller or any person in whom the Contract may have become vested and shall be entitled to the return of any monies paid in advance.

21 **General conditions in the tender**
No conditions submitted or referred to by Seller when tendering shall form part of the Contract unless otherwise agreed to in writing by Buyer.

22 **Applicable law**
This Contract shall be subject to English Law and the parties submit to the exclusive jurisdiction of the English Courts.

23 **Notices**
Any notice to be sent under this Agreement should be sent to the addresses given on page one and served personally or by pre-paid registered or recorded delivery letter or fax confirmed by first class post. Letters shall be deemed served 48 hours after posting and faxes on despatch.

24 **Waiver**
No delay or omission by Buyer in exercising any of its rights or remedies under this Agreement or under any applicable law on any occasion shall be deemed a waiver of, or bar to, the exercise of such right or remedy or any othe right or remedy upon any other occasion.

25 **Headings**
The headings in this Agreement are for ease of reference only and shall not affect the construction thereof.

26 **Severance**
In the event that any provision of this Agreement shall be void or unenforceable by reason of any provision or applicable law, it shall be deleted and the remaining provisions hereof shall continue in full force and effect and, if necessary, be so amended as shall be necessary to give effect to the spirit of the Agreement so far as possible.

Guidance notes on the use of Model Four:

'General Conditions of Contract for Services or Minor Works'

1 Use
Use for General Services work, (eg Office Cleaning, Window Cleaning, Gardening, Painting), Minor Repairs and Maintenance (eg Buildings, Fences, Water and Electrical Services), etc.

Note: In this form of contract the usual practice is to refer to the Buyer as the 'Employer', and to the Seller as the 'Contractor' even though this is not strictly an employment contract.

2 General note on negotiation
Always specify in the enquiry that it is a condition of the order that these Conditions are to be accepted. If the Contractor raises any objections these can then be the basis for negotiation. Avoid attempting to amend the Contractor's conditions to meet the Employer's requirements (see Part One, Section 1.4).

3 Definition of requirements
The following information should be part of any enquiry and/or purchase order:

3.1 Define carefully the work to be performed.

3.2 Date by which completion is required; be specific (see Part One, Section 5 − Seller's default) or, in the case of a regular service, the period for which the contract will run.

3.3 Terms of payment (see note 4.2).

3.4 Whether price is fixed or subject to a price-adjustment formula (see note 4.2).

3.5 State what utilities and other facilities (water, electricity, canteen accommodation, welfare, etc.) will be provided by the Employer.

3.6 Define the Contractor's site responsibilities (see note 4.1).

3.7 Specify who is responsible for off-loading and storage and what notice and arrangements are required for acceptance of delivery.

3.8 Stipulate any restrictions to be imposed on sub-letting (see note 4.3).

3.9   Specify any material which is to be 'free-issue'.

4 Notes on certain clauses

4.1   Clause 3 − 'Inspection of Site':
To avoid complications at a later stage it is essential that the Contractor visits the site to discuss all aspects of the Contract. The enquiry should include such an instruction; remember to specify the person to whom the Contractor should report.

4.2   Clause 6 − 'Terms of payment' (see Part One, Section 4)

(a) The terms of payment *must* be specified on the order. Usually the basis will be one of the following:

(i)   an 'all-in' fixed price
(ii) an 'all-in' price subject to a price-adjustment formula.
(iii) a price for equipment with separate rates for site work/attendance (eg time and materials).

(b) Although it it recommended practice to obtain a 'fixed price', it may be more economical in the case of long-term contracts to agree a price subject to a price-adjustment formula. This may work out cheaper than a 'pre-loaded' firm price. When considering price-adjustment formulae it is advisable to opt for a nationally recognised system such as the BEAMA CPA formula (see Part One, Section 4).

(c) A price basis of 'time and materials', whilst satisfactory for a small repair one-off job, is almost always the most expensive for the Employer since there is no incentive for the Contractor to work quickly.

4.3   Clause 8 − 'Assignment and sub-letting':
If it is anticipated that the Contractor intends to sub-let a significant part of the work then the details must be discussed and agreed with the Contractor before the order is placed.

4.4   Clause 11 − 'Payments to site labour':
The Contractor is required to obtain the Employer's approval of his proposed arrangements for paying his labour, ie working hours, rate or pay, bonuses, etc. These proposals should be made in writing and the Employer's agreement confirmed in writing either by letter or by inserting the details in the specification or Purchase Order.

The clause is relevant in the case of long-term contracts or 'time and material' work, but it can be deleted where fixed prices are agreed.

4.5   Clauses 14-16 — 'Indemnity/Insurances/Notifications':
These clauses set out proposed wording to safeguard the Employer but guidance should be sought from one's own broker regarding the value and extent of the cover required from the Contractor under clause 15.1(a). However, make sure that the clause 15.2 is put into effect.

4.6   Clause 21 — 'Loan of Employer's plant and equipment':
Any plant and equipment on hire to the Employer from a third party must *not* be loaned to the Contractor as this may invalidate the hire agreement and put the Employer at risk. No insurance cover is available for any loss or damage that could occur whilst such plant is being used by the Contractor.

4.7   Clause 23 — 'Insolvency and bankruptcy':
This clause reflects the Insolvency Act 1985 which introduced the terms 'administrative receiver' and 'administrator' appointed by a Court. Among the reasons why an administrator might be appointed are:

(a) to continue the company in whole or in part
(b) to optimise assets for liquidation

Model Four

General Conditions of Contract
for Services or Minor Works

1 Definitions

1.1   The term 'Employer' shall mean the person, firm or company so named in the Purchase Order.

1.2   The term 'Contractor' shall mean the person, firm or company to whom the Purchase Order is issued.

1.3   The 'Works' shall mean all work to be undertaken, and materials to be supplied, by the Contractor in performance of the Contract.

1.4   'The Site' shall mean the location where the Works are to be performed.

1.5   The term 'Purchase Order' shall mean the Employer's Purchase Order which specifies that these conditions apply to it.

1.6   'The Contract' shall mean the contract between the Employer and the Contractor consisting of the Purchase Order, these conditions and any other documents (or parts thereof) specified in the Purchase Order. Should there be any inconsistency between the documents comprising the contract, they shall have precedence in the order herein listed.

2 Inclusions in contract

The Contract includes for all materials, labour, plant, equipment, transport, handling of materials and plant, tools and appliances and all other things necessary for the Works.

3 Inspection of site

The Contractor is deemed to have understood the nature and extent of the Works, and to have visited the Site and shall make no claim founded on his failure to do so. The Employer shall, on request of the Contractor, grant such access as may be reasonable for this purpose.

4 Manner of carrying out the works

4.1   The Contractor shall make no delivery nor commence work on Site before obtaining the Employer's consent.

4.2   Access to and possession of the Site shall not be exclusive to the Contractor but only such as shall enable him to carry out the Works concurrently with the execution of work by others.

4.3   The Employer shall have the power at any time during the progress of the Works to order in writing:

(a) The removal from the Site of any materials which in the opinion of the Employer are not in accordance with the Contract.

(b) The substitution of proper and suitable materials.

(c) The removal and proper re-execution (notwithstanding any previous test thereof or interim payment therefor) of any work which, in respect of material or workmanship, is not in the opinion of the Employer in accordance with the Contract.

4.4   No work shall be laid in excavation and no work shall be covered or hidden until approved by the Employer.

5 Completion date

The date of completion of the Works or, in the case of a service being performed at regular intervals, the period of the Contract, shall be that specified in the Employer's Purchase Order unless otherwise agreed between the Employer and the Contractor. Time shall be of the essence.

6 Terms of payment

Unless otherwise stated in the Contract, payment will be made within 28 days of receipt and agreement of invoices, submitted monthly, for work completed to the satisfaction of the Employer.

Value Added Tax, where applicable, shall be shown separately on all invoices as a strictly nett extra charge.

7 Contractor's supervisor

The Contractor shall have a competent supervisor on the Site and any instructions given to the said supervisor (written or oral) shall be deemed to be given to the Contractor.

8 Assignment and sub-letting

8.1   The Contractor shall not assign or sub-let any portion of the Contract without the prior written consent of the Employer. No sub-letting shall relieve the Contractor from the responsibility of the Contract or from active supervision of the Works during their progress.

8.2   Where the Employer has consented to the placing of sub-contracts, copies of each sub-order shall be sent by the Contractor to the Employer immediately it is issued.

9 Variation in contract price

Save as provided for under Sub-Clause 10.2 the contract price shall be a firm price unless otherwise agreed between the parties when the Purchase Order is placed.

10 Variation of the works

10.1 The Contractor shall not vary any of the Works, except as directed in writing by the Employer.

10.2 The Employer reserves the right by notice in writing to modify the quality or quantity of the Works and any alteration to the Contract price arising by reason of such modification shall be agreed between the parties.

11 Payments to site labour

11.1 The Contractor and his Sub-Contractor (if any) shall pay their respective employees on the Site the rates of wages, and observe hours and conditions of working, recognised by the national agreements if any, for the industries or trades applicable to the Contractor's work and in any event at least the statutory minimum wage where in force and relevant. In the absence of such Agreements the Contractor and his Sub-Contractors shall observe rates and conditions approved by the Employer.

11.2 Bonus and other payments outside those defined in 11.1 above shall only be made in accordance with principles agreed with the Employer.

11.3 Hours of working, including overtime, shall be agreed with the Employer.

11.4 Before the placing of the Contract, the Contractor shall have obtained for himself and his Sub-Contractors (if any) the approval of the Employer for the arrangements covered in 11.1, 11.2 and 11.3 above. The Contractor and his Sub-Contractors shall not introduce or commence to negotiate any changes in these arrangements without the written consent of the Employer. Notice shall be given to the Employer of the implementation of any national awards affecting these arrangements.

11.5 The Contractor shall not offer employment to any person employed by the Employer or by other contractors employed by the Employer whilst work under the Contract is taking place.

12 Statutory duties and safety

12.1 The Works shall be carried out with the proper regard to safety and the

Contractor shall observe and conform to all statutory enactments and regulations and any by-laws and/or regulations of local or other authorities applicable to the Works or generally to the Site where the Works are carried out, the cost of supplying and/or doing all things required for the purpose being deemed to be included in the Contract price. Any additional expenses reasonably incurred by the Contractor in conforming with any such statutory enactments, by-laws and regulations made subsequently to the Contractor's tender shall be added to the Contract price, provided that such additional expenses were not ascertainable at the date of tender.

12.2 The Contractor shall also observe through his staff and work people the Works Rules (available on request) applicable to the Site where the Works are carried out. The Employer shall have the right to require the Contractor immediately on receipt of notice in writing to remove any of his employees on the Site who has:

(a) failed to comply with the Works Rules or

(b) in the opinion of the Employer misconducted himself, or been negligent or incompetent.

12.3 The Contractor shall be responsible for the suitability and safety of the equipment used by him and no equipment shall be used which may be unsuitable, unsafe or liable to cause damage. Without lessening the absolute responsibility of the Contractor in regard to such equipment the Employer shall have the right to inspect such equipment and if in the Employer's opinion it is unsuitable it shall not be used on the Works, no extra time or payment being allowed to the Contractor for replacement.

13 **Free-issue materials**

Where the Employer for the purposes of the contract issues materials free of charge to the Contractor such materials shall be and remain the property of the Employer. The Contractor shall maintain all such materials in good order and condition and shall use such materials solely in connection with the Contract. Any surplus materials shall be disposed of at the Employer's discretion. Waste of such materials arising from bad workmanship or negligence of the Contractor shall be made good at the Contractor's expense. Without prejudice to any other of the rights of the Buyer, Seller shall deliver up such materials whether further processed or not to the Buyer on demand.

14 **Indemnity**

The Contractor shall take every practicable precaution not to damage or injure any property or persons. The Contractor shall satisfy all claims founded on any such damage or injury which arise out of or in consequence of any operations under the Contract whether such claims are made by the Employer or by a third party against the Contractor or against the Employer, and the Contractor shall indemnify the Employer against all actions, demands, damages, costs, charges and expenses (including legal fees) arising in connection therewith, provided, however, that nothing in this condition shall render the Contractor liable for any injury or damage resulting from any negligent act or omission of the Employer, his servants or agents, or any other contractor employed by the Employer and the Employer shall indemnify the Contractor against all demands and expenses arising in connection with any such damage or injury.

15 Insurances

15.1 The Contractor shall have in force and shall require any Sub-Contractor to have in force:

(a) Employer's Liability Insurance and

(b) Public Liability Insurance for such sum and range of cover as the Contractor deems to be appropriate but not less than £500,000 for any one accident unless otherwise agreed by the Employer in writing.

All such insurances shall be extended to indemnify the Employer against any claim for which the Contractor or Sub-Contractor may be legally liable.

15.2 The Policy of Insurance shall be shown to the Employer whenever he requests together with satisfactory evidence of payment of premiums.

15.3 The Employer shall maintain Employer's Liability and Public Liability Insurance in respect of his own liabilities.

16 Notification procedure

The Contractor shall give immediate notice in the event of any accident or damage likely to form the subject of a claim under the Employer's insurance and shall give all the information and assistance in respect thereof that the Employer's insurers may require, and shall not negotiate, pay, settle, admit or repudiate any claim without their written consent, and shall permit the insurers to take proceedings in the name of the Contractor to recover compensation or secure an indemnity from any third party in respect of any of the matters covered by the said insurance.

17 Intellectual property rights

17.1 All patents, registered designs, design rights, copyright, trade marks and other intellectual property rights in the Works, goods or material produced for the Employer by the Contractor or its Sub-Contractors or specifically commissioned by the Employer from the Contractor shall vest in the Employer and the Contractor undertakes to execute all documents required to ensure such ownership and shall include a provision in its contract with the Sub-Contractor providing that ownership of such rights shall vest in the Employer (or the Contractor) and that the Sub-Contractors use only employees for undertaking such sub-contracted work.

17.2 Where the Contractor uses existing intellectual property of which it is the owner in the provision of the Works it hereby grants the Employer a licence to use the same and shall notify the Employer in writing of all such rights. It shall indemnify the Employer against all losses, costs and expenses, including legal fees on an indemnity basis, incurred by the Employer in using such rights, in particular, but without limitation, arising from third party actions or threatened actions for damages.

18 Contractor's conditions
No conditions submitted or referred to by the Contractor when tendering shall form part of the Contract unless otherwise agreed to in writing by the Employer.

19 Secrecy

19.1 No photographs of any of the Employer's equipment, installations or property shall be taken without the Employer's prior consent in writing. The Contractor shall keep secret and shall not divulge to any third party (except Sub-Contractors accepting a like obligation of secrecy, and then only to the extent necessary for the performance of the sub-contract) all information given by the Employer in connection with the Contract or which becomes known to the Contractor through his performance of such work under the Contract.

19.2 The Contractor shall not mention the Employer's name in connection with the Contract or disclose the existence of the Contract in any publicity material or other similar communication to third parties without the Employer's prior consent in writing.

20 Clearance of site on completion
On completion of the Works the Contractor shall remove at his expense his plant, equipment and unused materials and shall clear away from the Site all rubbish arising out of the Works.

21 Loan of employer's plant and equipment
(The inclusion of this condition does not imply that the Employer assumes any obligations to provide 'Loaned Plant', which means plant or equipment owned by the Employer and used by or on behalf of the Contractor by agreement.)

21.1 Where Loaned Plant is operated by a servant of the Employer:

(a) The Operator shall not become the servant of the Contractor but shall carry out with the Loaned Plant such work as he may be directed to do by the Contractor.

(b) The Contractor shall be liable for any damage to the Loaned Plant caused by misdirection or misuse of it due to negligence on the part of the Contractor, his servants or agents.

(c) The Employer shall be liable for any damage to the Loaned Plant caused by a defect in or faulty operation of the plant.

21.2 Where Loaned Plant is operated by a servant of the Contractor or an independent Contractor, the Contractor shall be liable for all damage to the Loaned Plant unless he can show that it was caused by a defect in the plant at the commencement of the loan and he shall be liable for any loss (including loss by theft) of the said plant.

21.3 The Employer shall have the right to withdraw Loaned Plant at any time and shall be under no liability whatever in connection with the Employer failing to lend plant at any time.

21.4 The Contractor shall satisfy himself that any Loaned Plant is suitable for the purpose intended.

22 Contractor's default

22.1 If the Contractor fails to carry out promptly any of the Employer's instructions, and fails within 10 days of notice by the Employer drawing attention to such failure to take such steps as reasonably satsify the Employer, the Employer may, without prejudice to any other of his rights, carry out Works at the risk and expense of the Contractor.

22.2 If the Contractor commits a breach of the Contract and fails within 10 days of notice by the Employer to take such steps as reasonably satisfy the Employer to rectify such breach, the Employer may, without prejudice to any other of his rights, terminate the Contact forthwith by notice to the Contractor. Thereupon, without prejudice to any other of his rights, the Employer may himself complete the Works or have it completed by a third party, using for that purpose (or making a fair and proper payment thereof) all materials, plant and equipment on the Site belonging to the Contractor, and the Employer shall not be liable to make any further payment to the Contractor until the Works have been completed in accordance with the requirements of the Contract, and shall be entitled to deduct from the Contract price (ascertained in accordance with the terms and conditions of the Contract) any additional cost incurred by the Employer. If the total cost to the Employer exceeds the said Contract price, the difference shall be recoverable by the Employer from the Contractor.

23 Insolvency and bankruptcy

If the Contractor becomes insolvent or bankrupt or (being a Company) makes an arrangement with its creditors or has an administrative receiver or administrator appointed or commences to be wound up (other than for the purposes of amalgamation or reconstruction) the Employer may, without prejudice to any other of his rights, terminate the Contract forthwith by notice to the Contractor or any person in whom the Contract may have become vested.

24 Construction of contract

The construction, validity and performance of the Contract shall be governed by the law of England and the parties agree to submit to the exclusive jurisdiction of the English Courts.

25 Notices

Any notice to be sent under this Agreement should be sent to the addresses given on page one and served personally or by pre-paid registered or recorded delivery letter or facsimile confirmed by first class post. Letters shall be deemed served 48 hours after posting and facsimiles on despatch.

26 Waiver

No delay or omission by Buyer in exercising any of its rights or remedies under this Agreement or under any applicable law on any occasion shall be deemed a waiver of, or bar to, the exercise of such right or remedy or any other right or remedy upon any other occasion.

27 Headings

The headings in this Agreement are for ease of reference only and shall not affect the construction thereof.

28 Severance

In the event that any provision of this Agreement shall be void or unenforceable by reason of any provision or applicable law, it shall be deleted and the remaining provisions hereof shall continue in full force and effect and, if necessary, be so amended as shall be necessary to give effect to the spirit of the Agreement so far as possible.

Model Five

Form of Agreement for Contract Staff

The following terms and conditions are agreed between ....
of .... (the 'Hirer') and .... of ....
('the Contract Agency') to apply to all staff ('Contract Staff') supplied by the
contract Agency.

1 **Hirer's responsibilities**
   Hirer will be responsible for the provision of working accommodation,
   canteen and medical facilities to the extent that such are provided for the
   Hirer's employees.

2 **Responsibilities of contract agency**
   It is the responsibility of the Contract Agency to ensure that Contract Staff
   know of and understand the requirements of this Agreement. Contract
   Staff shall:

   2.1 undertake design, drawing office or other technical, clerical or
        commercial work as directed by the Hirer including, when necessary,
        visits to the Hirer's works or other locations.

   2.2 work the same normal hours as the Hirer's staff employed at .....
        .... At present this means a normal week
        of .... hours, but any reasonable changes will be
        accepted by Contract Staff on being given reasonable advance notice by
        the Hirer.

   2.3 work outside normal hours if so required on being given reasonable
        advance notice by the Hirer.

   2.4 notify the Hirer, in advance where possible, of any intention to be absent
        from work.

   2.5 observe the rules applicable to the Hirer's staff.

3 **Hire charges**

   3.1 The Hirer shall pay the Contract Agency a basic hourly rate to be agreed
        at the time of hire of Contract Staff. This rate shall be exclusive of Value
        Added Tax (where applicable) but it shall be fully inclusive of such items
        as subsistence and lodging allowances, travelling expenses (except those
        incurred by specific visits requested by the Hirer), sickness benefits,
        National Insurance contributions, holidays with pay etc.

Expenses incurred in temporary work at a site other than that defined at the time of hire will be defrayed at net cost by the Hirer direct to the contract Satff in accordance with clause 7.

3.2   Work outside normal working hours, as and when requested by the Hirer, worked during the normal working week (Monday to Friday) will be paid at the basic hourly rate defined in 3.1 above.

Saturday, Sunday, and Bank Holiday working will be paid at the basic hourly rate plus . . . .

3.3   The Hirer will make no payment for the time Contract Staff are absent from work.

4 **Time sheets**
Unless otherwise agreed weekly time sheets shall be provided by the Contract Agency for each of the Contract Staff. The hours worked by each person shall be recorded on the time sheets which shall be prepared in duplicate. Both sheets will be signed by an authorised representative of the Hirer, one copy being retained by the Hirer and the other returned to the Contract Agency.

5 **Payment**
The Contract Agency shall submit invoices cross-referenced to the approved time sheets at . . . . intervals. Value Added Tax (where applicable) shall be shown separately on each invoice as a strictly net extra charge.

The Hirer shall make payment by the close of the month following the month of receipt of invoice unless otherwise agreed at the time of hire.

6 **Notice of termination of hire**

6.1   Termination by the Hirer − The Hirer shall have the right to require the Contract Agency to withdraw the services of any Contract Staff at the expiration of a minimum period of . . . . from the date of notice in writing to this effect given by the Hirer to the Contract Agency and, in the event of a breach of discipline or of misconduct on the part of any one of the Contract Staff, or if the Hirer shall not be satisfied that any person will observe the conditions as to secrecy imposed from time to time by the Hirer, then the Hirer shall have the right to require the Contract Agency immediately to withdraw that person and the services of such a person shall not be offered for hire thereafter for any work for the Hirer.

6.2   Termination by Contract Agency − the Contract Agency shall give notice in writing to the Hirer of its intention to withdraw the services of any of the Contract Staff at the expiration of a minimum period of . . . . from the date of such notice.

7 Travel requested by the Hirer

Should any Contract Staff be required to travel at the specific request of the Hirer they will be expected to do so under the conditions applicable to the Hirer's staff. Briefly these are that the Hirer will pay second-class fares and reasonable hotel and out-of-pocket expenses. The hotel bills, receipts for meals and for all except sundry expenses must be submitted to the Hirer with the claim for reimbursement of expenses.

Occasions may arise when an individual uses his own car for business purposes associated with the Hirer's work, in which case payment will be made by the Hirer in accordance with its provisions for mileage allowance current at that time. The individual shall ensure that his Motor Policy permits business use under such circumstances and shall further satisfy the Hirer that the cover extends to indemnify the Hirer as Principal.

Payment for time spent travelling outside normal working hours shall be at the discretion of the Hirer.

8 Indemnity and insurance

8.1 The Contract Agency shall satisfy all claims founded on any damage to any property or any persons which arise out of or in consequence of the presence of the Contract Staff on the premises of the Hirer or their activities hereunder whether such claims are made by the Hirer or by a third party against the Contract Agency or the Hirer, and the Contract Agency shall indemnify the Hirer against all payments and expenses arising in connection therewith provided that the Contract Agency shall not be liable for damage which results from any act or neglect of the Hirer, his servants or agents.

8.2 The Contract Agency shall have in force Public Liability (Third Party) insurance for such sum and range of cover as the Contract Agency shall consider appropriate, but for no less than £500,000 in respect of any one accident. Such insurance shall indemnify the Hirer as Principal against any claim for which the Contract Agency may be liable.

9 Inventions

Inventions, works, software, designs or other materials in which there are intellectual property rights made by Contract Staff, either alone or jointly with any other person whilst engaged on work under this Agreement shall belong to the Hirer absolutely and the individual shall give all assistance in his power including the execution of all necessary documents to procure the vesting of such inventions in the Hirer as absolute owner, and the maintenance and extension of such patents and other rights. After leaving the service of the Hirer the individual shall be under a continuing obligation to sign documents and render all reasonable assistance to the Hirer pursuant to letters patent for such inventions. The Contract Agency undertakes to ensure its contract with Contract

Staff contains terms to this effect and direct deed to this effect with Hirer where the Hirer so requires.

10 **Secrecy**
Contract Staff will be required to sign an undertaking as a deed not to disclose information relating to the Hirer's business and interests to any other party and Contract Agency shall undertake that they do so.

11 **Applicable law**
This contract shall be subject to English Law and the parties submit to the exclusive jurisdiction of the English Courts.

12 **Contract Staff not Employees of Hirer**
Contract Staff shall continue to be employed by Contract Agency and not the Hirer. Contract Agency undertakes to pay Contract Staff's national insurance and tax under PAYE, sick pay, holiday pay and the like.

13 **Notices**
Any notice to be sent under this Agreement should be sent to the addresses given on page one and served personally or by pre-paid registered or recorded delivery letter or facsimile confirmed by first class post. Letters shall be deemed served 48 hours after posting and facsimiles on despatch.

14 **Waiver**
No delay or omission by Buyer in exercising any of its rights or remedies under this Agreement or under any applicable law on any occasion shall be deemed a waiver of, or bar to, the exercise of such right or remedy or any other right or remedy upon any other occasion.

15 **Headings**
The Headings in this Agreement are for ease of reference only and shall not affect the construction thereof.

16 **Severance**
In the event that any provision of this Agreement shall be void or unenforceable by reason of any provision or applicable law, it shall be deleted and the remaining provisions hereof shall continue in full force and effect and, if necessary, be so amended as shall be necessary to give effect to the spirit of the Agreement so far as possible.

Signed for and on behalf of the Hirer

. . . .

Signed for and on behalf of the Contract Agency

. . . .

Date . . . .

Model Six

Secrecy Deed of Undertaking

I, the undersigned, undertake as a deed that in consideration of being permitted to undertake work for the Hirer under an Agreement between the Hirer and . . .

. . . . dated . . . .

I will:

1 Keep strictly confidential all secrets of the Hirer (which shall be deemed to include the secrets of any company, firm or person with which the Hirer may be in commercial or technical co-operation or association) and I will not either during the period of my work for the Hirer, or at any time afterwards, divulge any information relating in any way whatsoever to the business or interest of the Hirer to any third party or make use of such information to the detriment or prejudice of the Hirer.

2 Obey any directions of the Hirer and follow any procedures laid down by the Hirer for protecting the security of information.

3 Obtain written permission from the Hirer, or his authorised representative, before publishing any literature, delivering any lecture or making any communication with the Press relating to Hirer's products or any matter with which the Hirer may be concerned.

4 Not take photographs of the Hirer's property without written permission from an authorised representative of the Hirer.

5 Not, without the approval and permission of an authorised representative of the Hirer, remove from the Hirer's premises any drawings, documents or prints thereof to display as examples of my workmanship to other potential customers for my services.

6 And I acknowledge that any discoveries, inventions, improvements, software, works, processes, designs, drawings, trade marks, calculations, formulae or documents whether patentable or not, made, discovered or developed by me in the course of or by reason of my work for the Hirer are the property of the Hirer and are to be considered as confidential information of the Hirer and I shall register no rights therein. I will at the request and cost of the Hirer at any time take all steps and execute all documents necessary to enable the Hirer to obtain patent or corresponding protection in respect of such of the above as may be susceptible of such protection.

Signed as a deed by ....

Address ....

Witnessed by ....

Address ....

Date ....

Outline of procedure to be adopted when hiring Contract Staff (see Model Conditions 5 and 6)

The following two documents have been prepared for use when hiring contract staff:

1 'Form of Agreement for Contract Staff' agreement between the Hirer and a Contract Agency. (Model Conditions Five)

2 'Secrecy Undertaking' to be signed by each of the Contract Staff. (Model Conditions Six)

The documents apply to all forms of contract staff – typists, clerical, laboratory, engineering or commercial – and it is recommended that the procedure set out below is observed.

1 **Items to be agreed with Contract Agency:**

(a) Normal working hours (see Clause 2.2).

(b) Basic hourly rate (see Clause 3.1). The method of apportioning this rate betwen contract staff salary and agency profit is left to the discretion of the Hirer.

(c) Rate for Saturday, Sunday or Bank Holiday working (see Clause 3.2).

(d) Who provides time sheets (see Clause 4) and interval for their submission (see Clause 5)?

(e) Minimum period of notice required for termination of hire (see Clause 6).

(f) Number of staff required and starting date.

2 **Agreement Form:**

(a) Complete two copies of the Agreement inserting details of the Hirer and Contract Agency in the first paragraph. Fill in the blanks in Clauses 2.2, 3.2, 5, 6.1, and 6.2.

The Secrecy Undertaking is signed as a "deed" because otherwise it would not be enforceable in law between the Contract Staff individual and the business contracting with the Contract Agency. There is no consideration - money or moneys worth - passing between the individual and the business contracting with the Contract Agency; however if the contract is signed ad a "Deed" in the presence of a witness then the document can be enforced even though there is no consideration, as in law "Deeds' do no require consideration to be enforceable.

(b) Send two copies of the Agreement (and for information, a copy of the Secrecy Deed of Undertaking) to the Contract Agency for signature.

(c) On receipt of the signed Agreement forms both copies should be countersigned for the Hirer by an authorised signatory.

(d) Return a completed Agreement to the Contract Agency together with a letter confirming the number of staff required, starting date and agreed hire charges. File one copy of Agreement and letter.

(e) Arrange for Purchase Order to be issued, where required.

3 Contract staff

(a) For each individual reporting for duty prepare two copies of the Secrecy Deed of Undertaking, inserting name of Contract Agency and Date of Agreement.

(b) Each individual has to read, sign and date both copies of the undertaking.

(c) One completed copy is given to the individual concerned, the other copy being filed.

(d) Where an individual is authorised to use his own car for business purposes in connection with the work the individual must produce evidence that his motor insurance policy permits such use and that the cover is extended to indemnify the hirer.

Guidance notes on the use of Model Seven

'Conditions of Contract for Dismantling and/or Demolition Contracts'

1 Use
Use for all contracts for **dismantling and/or demolition work** in connection with Buildings, Structures, Plant, Equipment, Pipework, Cables, etc.

Note: In this form of contract the usual practice is to refer to the Buyer as the 'Employer' and to the Seller as the 'Contractor'.

2 General note on negotiation
Always specify in the enquiry that it is a condition of the order that these Conditions are to be accepted. If the Contractor raises any objections these then can be the basis for negotiation. Avoid attempting to amend the Contractor's Conditions to meet one's own requirements (see Part One, Section 1.4).

3 Definition of requirements
The following information should be part of any enquiry and/or purchase order:

3.1   Description and specification of work required; and define the Site.

3.2   Work programme – starting and finishing dates; be specific (see Part One, Section 5 – Seller's default).

3.3   Specify any limitations, eg disruption of services; agree sequence of work where necessary; clearance certificate procedures and any other aspects not covered by 'Works Rules'.

3.4   The terms of payment (see note 4.7).

3.5   Whether price is fixed or subject to fluctuation – particularly important if plant hire rates are involved.

3.6   State what utilities and other facilities (accommodation, welfare, etc.) will be provided by the Employer.

3.7   Stipulate those items which have to be dismantled and returned to the Employer (see note 4.1).

3.8   Define Contractor's Site responsibilities (see notes 4.2 and 4.3).

3.9   Stipulate any restrictions to be imposed on sub-letting (see note 4.4).

3.10   Specify arrangements for the transport of dismantled/demolished materials (by specified Site roads to works gate) including 'pass-out' documentation.

3.11   Specify responsibility for maintaining and upholding footpaths and roads in the area of the Contractor's operations.

3.12   Specify disposal requirements for such debris as concrete, brickwork, lagging (particularly for asbestos-bearing materials), etc., if necessary.

3.13   Stipulate any special requirements for the avoidance of nuisance, eg dust-water sprinkling; noise restriction; fire and smoke; vibration — particularly that arising from the use of heavy balls or explosives.

3.14   Specify any hazards inherent in any items to be dismantled/demolished, or present in the area of the work (see note 4.2).

3.15   Specify the normal hours of working appertaining to the Site (see Clause 15).

4   Notes on certain clauses

4.1   Clause 4 — 'Passing of property':
If there are any items like valves, pumps, motors, steelwork which the Employer wishes to retain after dismantling/demolition these must be specified to the Contractor at the enquiry stage and detailed on the Purchase Order.

4.2   Clause 5 — 'Inspection of Site':
The Employer has a statutory common duty of care towards all persons invited on to the property which imposes certain obligations on him with respect to their safety. The Occupiers Liability Act 1957 provides that he can transfer some of these obligations to the person so invited, provided that the person knowingly accepts them.

To avoid complications at a later stage it is essential that the Contractor visits the Site to discuss all aspects of the Contract. The enquiry should include such an instruction; remember to specify the person to whom the Contractor should report.

The discussions, which should be recorded, should highlight any hidden cables, drains, mains or the like which need to be safeguarded and any services passing through or over the area of operations which have to be maintained.

4.3   Clause 6 – 'Manner of carrying out the Works':
The type of equipment and methods of working the Contractor intends to use must be agreed before work commences (Clause 6.3). The areas available to the Contractor for depositing plant and/or materials must be agreed (Clause 6.7).

4.4   Clause 10 – 'Assignment and sub-letting':
Establish whether the Contractor wishes to sub-let a significant part of the work. If so, the details must be discussed and agreed with the Contractor before the order is placed.

4.5   Clause 16 – 'Payments to site labour':
The Contractor is required to obtain the Employer's approval of his proposed arrangements for paying his labour, ie working hours, rates of pay, bonuses, etc. These proposals should be made in writing and the Employer's agreement confirmed in writing either by letter or by inserting the details in the specification or Purchase Order.

4.6   Clauses 18 and 19 – 'Indemnity' and 'Contractor's insurance':
These clauses set out proposed wording to safeguard the Employer, but guidance should be sought from one's own broker regarding the value and extent of the cover required from the Contractor under clause 19.1 (2). However, make sure that the clause 19.2 is put into effect.

4.7   Clause 22 – 'Terms of payment' (see Part One, Section 4):
The terms of payment *must* be specified on the Purchase Order.

(a) Where the Contract value is less than say £20,000:

(i) If the Contractor is to pay the Employer then payment in full should be required before the Contractor is given possession of the Site.

(ii) If the Employer is to pay the Contractor then payment should be made after the completion of the Contract.

(b) Where the contract value exceeds say £20,000.

For large jobs stage payments may be reasonable in particular circumstances. The enquiry should indicate the Employer's intentions. Such stage payments should be related to, and conditional upon, work done.

4.8   Clause 24 – 'Secrecy':
This clause is primarily intended to safeguard information which becomes known to the Contractor during his operations on Site. However, it is

possible for someone with a knowledge of manufacturing plant/processes to obtain vital information from materials after they have been removed from the Site. This aspect is particularly important where plant items can be removed virtually intact.

Thus in some instances, to protect certain process knowledge, it may be necessary to instruct the Contractor to cut up or otherwise destroy some plant items before removal from Site, such that the materials can only be disposed of as scrap.

Such instructions should be given at the enquiry stage since there may well be a significant effect on price.

4.9   Clause 27 − 'Insolvency and bankruptcy':
This clause reflects the Insolvency Act 1985 which introduced the term 'administrative receiver' and 'administrator' appointed by a Court. Among the reasons why an administrator might be appointed are:

(a)   to continue the company in whole or in part

(b)   to optimise assets for liquidation

4.10   Clause 28 − 'Loan of Buyer's plant and equipment':
Any plant and equipment on hire to the Employer from a third party must *not* be loaned to the Contractor as this may invalidate the hire agreement and put the Employer at risk. No insurance cover is available for any loss or damage that could occur whilst such plant is being used by the Contractor.

Model Seven

Conditions of Contract for Dismantling and/or Demolition Contracts

1 Definitions

1.1 The term 'Employer' shall mean the Company so named in the Employer's Purchase Order.

1.2 The term 'Contractor' shall mean the person, firm or company to whom the Purchase Order is issued.

1.3 The 'Works' shall mean both the dismantling and/or demolition work the subject of the Contract and the building, plant or property to be dismantled or demolished.

1.4 'The Site' shall mean the location where the Works are to be performed.

1.5 The term 'Purchase Order' shall mean Employer's Purchase Order which specifies that these conditions apply to it.

1.6 'The Contract' shall mean the contract between the Employer and the Contractor consisting of the Purchase Order, these conditions and any other documents (or parts thereof) specified in the Purchase Order. Should there be any inconsistency between the documents comprising the Contract, they shall have precedence in the order herein listed.

2 Inclusions in contract price

The Contract price includes for all materials, labour, plant, equipment, transport, handling of materials and plant and equipment, and for the accommodation necessary for the complete dismantling, demolition, disposal of all metal and other materials and debris, guarding, watching and lighting and for all insurance called for, or necessary to cover, the Contractor's liabilities under the Contract, and the statutory duties and safety provisions as detailed in Clause 17.

3 Completion date

The date of completion of the Works shall be that specified in the Purchase Order unless agreed otherwise in writing between the Employer and the Contractor. Time shall be of the essence. When requested by the Employer the Contractor shall submit a programme for the Works giving details of his proposals for carrying out the Works within the time stipulated indicating the sequence and timing of all operations forming part of the Works.

4 Passing of property

All materials and debris arising out of the Works shall (unless otherwise specified in the Purchase Order) become the property of the Contractor from the moment when the same are permanently removed from the Employer's premises but the Employer excludes all liability, same that which may not in law be excluded, in relation to such materials and debris and makes no warranty about their safety, quality, quantity, provenance or resale value, if any.

5 Inspection of Site

The Contractor is deemed to have understood the nature and extent of the Works, and to have visited the Site and shall make no claim founded on his failure to do so. The Employer shall, on request of the Contractor, grant such access as may be reasonable for this purpose. The Contractor shall be deemed to have willingly accepted the risks of the Works.

6 Manner of carrying out the Works

6.1 The Contractor shall on being given possession of the Site forthwith proceed with the Works and duly complete the same by the completion date with the proper despatch and workmanship and in all respects in accordance with the terms of the Contract.

6.2 No service may be disconnected or diverted without the prior approval in writing of the Employer.

6.3 The type of equipment and methods of working that the Contractor intends to use shall be subject to the approval in writing of the Employer and no work on the Site shall commence until such approval has been obtained but such approval shall not relieve the Contractor from any of his obligations under the Contract.

6.4 The Contractor shall take full responsibility for the Works during the execution of the Contract and shall ensure that on completion the Site shall conform in all respects to the requirements of the Contract.

6.5 The Contractor shall not interfere with the operation of any plant or services not included in the Works without the prior approval in writing of the Employer.

6.6 The Works are to be carried out without damage to remaining parts of the structure or adjoining plants or buildings, and if such damage shall occur in the carrying out of the Works the Contractor shall reinstate and make good the same at his own expense. All such making good shall be executed so as to match in every respect the surrounding work and be properly bonded thereto.

6.7 The Contractor shall not use any part of the Employer's premises for depositing plant, materials or dismantled structures arising out of or necessary for the execution of the Works without the prior approval in writing of the Employer.

7 Contract information to be confidential

All plans, drawings, designs or specifications supplied by the Employer to the Contractor shall remain the property of, and shall be returned to, the Employer on completion of the Contract and shall not be copied, and no information relating to the Works shall be disclosed to any third party except for the purpose of this Contract.

8 Contractor's supervisor

The Contractor shall have a competent supervisor on the Works and any instructions given to him (written or oral) shall be deemed to be given to the Contractor.

9 Inspection

The Employer may at all reasonable times inspect any part of the Works and the Contractor shall comply with all reasonable requests made by the Employer. Nothing in this Clause shall, however, relieve the Contractor from his obligations under the Contract.

10 Assignment and sub-letting

The Contractor shall not assign or sub-let any portion of the Contract without the prior written consent of the Employer. No sub-letting shall relieve the Contractor from the responsibility of the Contract or from active supervision of the Works during their progress.

11 Suspension of Works

The Contractor shall suspend the whole of the Works or any part thereof on the instructions of the Employer. Any additional cost proved by the Contractor to have arisen from such suspension shall be paid by the Employer.

12 Explosives and naked lights

12.1 No explosives or naked lights shall be used without the written consent of the Employer.

12.2 When burning gear is used care shall be taken to ensure that no fires are started or left smouldering when workmen leave the Site. Burning of rubbish shall not be permitted.

13 Contract price

13.1 Save as provided for under Clause 14 the Contract price shall, unless otherwise agreed, be a firm price and shall include all the requirements referred to in Clause 2 and no variation shall be allowed unless agreed in writing by the Employer.

13.2 Where it is agreed that the Contract shall be on the basis of a price per unit weight, all empty vehicles shall be tared and all loaded vehicles weighed on the Employer's or Employer's designated weighbridge and the Contractor shall accept these weights as final. The Contractor may at his option witness such weighing operations.

14 Variation of the Works

The Employer reserves the right by notice in writing to modify the Works, and any alterations in the Contract Price caused by such modification shall be agreed in writing between the Employer and the Contractor.

15 Hours of working and overtime

The Works shall be executed within the normal hours of working on the Site but a departure from these hours may be agreed in writing between the Employer and the Contractor. Overtime beyond such agreed hours shall only be resorted to on the specific instructions of the Employer. Where the Contractor is required to resort to such overtime working for reasons under his control, no additional payment shall be made by the Employer. If the Employer instructs the Contractor to work such overtime for other reasons, the Employer shall pay to the Contractor the net extra cost of the overtime premium payments.

16 Payments to Site labour

16.1 The Contractor and his Sub-Contractors (if any) shall pay their respective employees on the Site the rates of wages, and observe hours and conditions of working, recognised by any of the national agreements for the industries or trades applicable to the Contractor's work and, where in force and applicable, the national minimum wage. In the absence of such agreements the Contractor and his sub-contractors shall observe rates and conditions approved by the Employer. Such employees are not employees of the Employer.

16.2 Bonus and other payments outside those defined in 16.1 above shall only be made in accordance with principles agreed with the Employer.

16.3 Hours worked, including overtime, shall be agreed with the Employer.

16.4 Before the placing of the Contract, the Contractor shall have obtained for himself and his sub-contractors (if any) the approval in writing of the Employer for the arrangements covered in 16.1, 16.2, and 16.3 above. The Contractor and his sub-contractors shall not introduce or commence to negotiate any changes in these arrangements without the written consent of the Employer. Notice shall be given to the employer of the implementation of any national awards affecting these arrangements.

17 Statutory duties and safety

17.1 The Works shall be carried out with the proper regard to safety. The Contractor shall observe and conform to all statutory enactments and regulations and any by-laws and/or regulations of local or other authorities applicable to the Works or generally to the Site where the Works are carried out. Any additional expenses reasonably incurred by the Contractor in conforming with any statutory enactments, by-laws and regulations made subsequently to the Contractor's tender shall be added to the Contract price, provided that such additional expenses were not ascertainable at the date of tender.

17.2 The Contractor shall observe through his staff and work people the 'Works Rules' (available on request) applicable to the Site where the Works are carried out. The Employer shall have the right to require the Contractor immediately on receipt of notice in writing to remove any of his employees on the Site who has:

(a) failed to comply with the Works Rules or

(b) has, in the opinion of the Employer, misconducted himself or been negligent or incompetent.

17.3 The Contractor shall be responsible for the suitability and safety of the equipment used by him and no equipment shall be used which may be unsuitable, unsafe or liable to cause damage. If in the Employer's opinion any equipment is unsuitable it shall not be used on the Works, no extra time or payment being allowed to the Contractor for replacement.

18 Indemnities – persons, property, highways and transport

18.1 All operations necessary for the execution of the Works shall be carried out so as not to:

(a) damage or injure any property adjoining the Works or other property, or persons, or

(b) interfere unnecessarily or improperly with the convenience of the public or access to or use of public or private goods or property, or

(c) create any unreasonable or unlawful noise or disturbance

and the Contractor shall satisfy all claims founded thereupon which arise out or in consequence of any operations under the Contract whether such claims are made by the Employer or by a third party against the Contractor or against the Employer, and the Contractor shall indemnify the Employer against all actions, demands, damages, costs, charges and expenses arising in connection therewith provided, however, that nothing in this clause shall render the Contractor liable for any claim in connection therewith arising from any unlawful or negligent act or omission of the Employer, his servants or agents, or any other contractor (not being employed by the Contractor).

18.2 The Contractor shall use every reasonable means to prevent any of the highways or bridges communicating with or on the routes to the Site from being subjected to extraordinary traffic within the meaning of the Highways Act 1959 or in Scotland the Road Traffic Act 1930 or any statutory modification or re-enactment thereof by any traffic of the Contractor or his sub-contractors. In particular he shall select routes and use vehicles and restrict and distribute loads so that any such extraordinary traffic arising from the moving of plant materials or dismantled structures to and from the Site shall be limited as fas as is reasonably possible and so that no damage or injury may be caused to such highways and bridges.

18.3 Unless otherwise provided for in the Contract the Contractor shall be responsible for and shall pay the cost of strengthening any bridges or altering or improving any highways communicating with the Site to facilitate the movement of plant, materials or dismantled structures arising out of or necessary for the execution of the Works, and the Contractor shall indemnify the Employer against all claims for damage to any highway or bridge caused by such movement including, without limitation, such claims as may be made by any competent authority directly against the Employer pursuant to any Act of Parliament or other Statutory Instrument.

18.4 If, notwithstanding 18.2 above, any damage shall occur to any bridge or highway arising from the movement of such plant, materials or dismantled structures the Contractor shall notify the Employer as soon as he becomes aware of such damage or receives any claim.

19 Insurances

19.1 The Contractor shall have in force and shall require any sub-contractor to have in force:

(a) Employer's Liability Insurance and

(b) Public Liability Insurance for such sum and range of cover as the Contractor deems to be appropriate but not less than £1,000,000 for any one accident unless otherwise agreed by the Employer in writing.

All such insurances shall be extended to indemnify the Employer against any claim for which the Contractor or sub-contractor may be legally liable.

19.2   The Policy of Insurance shall be shown to the Employer whenever he requests together with satisfactory evidence of payment of premiums.

19.3   The Employer shall maintain Employer's Liability and Public Liability Insurance in respect of his own liabilities.

20   Notification procedure

The Contractor shall give immediate notice in the event of any accident or damage likely to form the subject of a claim under the Employer's insurance and shall give all the information and assistance in respect thereof that the Employer's insurers may require, and shall not negotiate, pay, settle, admit or repudiate any claim without their written consent, and shall permit the insurers to take proceedings in the name of the Contractor to recover compensation or secure an indemnity from any third party in respect of any of the matters covered by the said insurance.

21   Facilities to other contractors

The Contractor shall afford all reasonable facilities of access to the Employer and any other of the Employer's contractors.

22   Terms of payment

The terms of payment shall be as stated in the Purchase Order. Value Added Tax, where applicable, shall be shown separately on all invoices as a strictly net extra charge.

23   Contractor's conditions

No conditions submitted or referred to by the Contractor shall form part of the Contract unless otherwise agreed to in writing by the Employer.

24   Secrecy

24.1   No photographs of any of the Employer's equipment, installations or property shall be taken without the Employer's prior consent in writing. The Contractor shall keep secret and shall not divulge to any third party (except Sub-Contractors accepting a like obligation of secrecy, and then only to the extent necessary for the performance of the sub-contract) all information given by the Employer in connection with the Contract or which becomes known to the Contractor through his performance of the Contract.

24.2   The Contractor shall not mention the Employer's name in connection with the Contract or disclose the existence of the Contract in any publicity material or other similar communication to third parties without the Employer's prior consent in writing.

25 Clearance of Site

25.1 The Contractor shall remove all materials and debris progressively as the Works proceed unless otherwise instructed by the Employer.

25.2 When required to do so the Contractor shall dispose of particular rubbish or other materials as instructed by the Employer.

25.3 On completion of the Works the Contractor shall leave the Site in a clean and safe condition with all holes suitably filled in and obstructions removed unless otherwise agreed in writing by the Employer.

26 Contractor's default or insolvency

26.1 If the Contractor fails to carry out promptly any of the Employer's instructions, and fails within ten days of notice by the Employer drawing attention to such failure to take such steps as reasonably satisfy the Employer, the Employer may, without prejudice to any other of his rights, carry out the Works at the risk and expense of the Contractor.

26.2 If the Contractor commits a breach of the Contract and fails within ten days of notice by the Employer to take such steps as reasonably satisfy the Employer to rectify such breach, the Employer may, without prejudice to any other of his rights, terminate the Contract forthwith by notice to the Contractor. Thereupon without prejudice to any other of his rights, the Employer may himself complete the Works or have them completed by a third party, using for that purpose (on making a fair and proper payment therefor) all materials, plant and equipment on the Site belonging to the Contractor. If in such event the total cost to the Employer of carrying out the Works is greater than the price to be paid therefor by the Employer under the Contract or (in cases where the Contract provides for payment by the Contractor to the Employer) if the total receipts of the Employer from the carrying out of the Works are less than the sum to be paid by the Contractor under the Contract, the Contractor shall forthwith on demand refund or pay to the Employer as the case may be the difference.

27 Insovency and bankruptcy

If the Contractor becomes insolvent or bankrupt or (being a Company) makes an arrangement with its creditors or has an administrative receiver or administrator appointed or commences to be wound up (other than for the purposes of amalgamation or reconstruction) the Employer may, without prejudice to any other of his rights, terminate the Contract forthwith by notice to the Contractor or any person in whom the Contract may have become vested.

28 Loan of Employer's plant and equipment

(The inclusion of this condition does not imply that the Employer assumes any obligation to provide 'Loaned Plant' which means plant or equipment owned by the Employer and used by or on behalf of the Contractor by agreement.)

28.1 Where Loaned Plant is operated by a servant of the Employer:

   (a) The operator shall not become the servant of the Contractor but shall carry out with the Loaned Plant such work as he may be directed to do by the Contractor.

   (b) The Contractor shall be liable for any damage to the Loaned Plant caused by misdirection or misuse of it due to negligence on the part of the Contractor, his servants or agents.

   (c) The Employer shall be liable for any damage to the Loaned Plant caused by a defect therein or faulty operation thereof.

28.2 Where Loaned Plant is operated by a servant of the Contractor or an independent contractor the Contractor shall be liable for all damage to the Loaned Plant unless he can show that it was caused by a defect present in the Plant at the commencement of the loan and he shall be liable for any loss (including loss by theft) of the said plant.

28.3 The Employer shall have the right to withdraw Loaned Plant at any time and shall be under no liability whatever in connection with the Employer failing to lend plant at any time.

28.4 The Contractor shall satisfy himself that any Loaned Plant is suitable for the purpose intended.

29 Construction of Contact

The construction, validity and performance of the Contract shall be governed by the law of England and the parties agree to submit to the exclusive jurisdiction of the English Courts.

30 Notices

Any notice to be sent under this Agreement should be sent to the addresses given on page one and served personally or by pre-paid registered or recorded delivery letter or fax confirmed by first class post. Letters shall be deemed served 48 hours after posting and faxes on despatch.

31 Waiver

No delay or omission by Buyer in exercising any of its rights or remedies under this Agreement or under any applicable law on any occasion shall be deemed a waiver of, or bar to, the exercise of such right or remedy or any other right or remedy upon any other occasion.

32 Headings
The headings in this Agreement are for ease of reference only and shall not affect the construction thereof.

33 Severance
In the event that any provision of this Agreement shall be void or unenforceable by reason of any provision or applicable law, it shall be deleted and the remaining provisions hereof shall continue in full force and effect and, if necessary, be so amended as shall be necessary to give effect to the spirit of the Agreement so far as possible.

Guidance notes on the use of Model Eight 'General Conditions of Contract for the Repair or Modification of Engineering Equipment'

1 Use
Use for **repair, overhaul or modification of engineering plant and equipment** whether the work is carried out *in situ* or returned to or manufactured at Contractor's Works.

Note: The format of the document has been so arranged that it can be considered as being in two parts. Clauses 1 to 19 inclusive are applicable to *all* enquiries and purchase orders, whereas Clauses 20 onwards are applicable only where some Site work is involved. Thus Clauses 20 to 28 inclusive should be deleted where all work is performed off Site.

2 General note on negotiation
Always specify in the enquiry that it is a condition of the order that these Conditions are to be accepted. If the Contractor raises any objections these can then be the basis for negotiation. Avoid attempting to amend the Contractor's conditions to meet one's own requirements (see Part One, Section 1.4).

3 Definition of requirements
The following information should be part of any enquiry and/or Purchase Order:

3.1   Description and specification of work required. Specify whether work is to be done on or off Site. It should be borne in mind that the principles given in note 4.8 (a) apply equally where the work is done 'off-site'.

3.2   Specify when the equipment to be repaired/modified will be available and the required completion date of the work (see Part One, Section 5 − Seller's Default). Be specific regarding any limitations on Site work, eg start and finish dates of plant shutdowns, etc. (see note 4.9).

3.3   For work done 'off site', give delivery point and, in the case of overseas suppliers, the ultimate destination.

3.4   Terms of payment (see note 4.2)

3.5   Whether price is fixed or subject to escalation.

3.6   Whether subject to Employer's inspection and expediting.

3.7   Comprehensive specification of all matters affecting the design, operating conditions, performance, duty, climatic conditions that the equipment when repaired or modified will be required to meet, ie fitness for purpose.

3.8   State what utilities and other facilities (accommodation, welfare, etc.) will be provided by the Employer.

3.9   Define the Contractor's Site responsibilities (see note 4.8)

3.10   For Site work, specify who is responsible for off-loading and storage and what notice and arrangements are required for acceptance of delivery.

3.11   Fabrication, erection and commissioning programme (as necessary).

3.12   Performance tests, procedure for acceptance and guarantees.

3.13   Stipulate any restrictions to be imposed on sub-letting (see note 4.6).

3.14   State any special or unusual requirements and any special markings required on materials or equipment.

3.15   Specify any material which is to be of 'free issue'.

3.16   Specify any special protection, packing or transport requirements.

4 **Notes on certain clauses**

4.1   Clause 4 − 'Passing of property and risk':

   4.1.1   Where the equipment is taken 'off site' it remains the Employer's property but the Contractor should have insurance to cover it against the usually expected risks, i.e. fire, theft, etc.; this point should be checked (see sub-clause 4.2).

   4.1.2   The Conditions provide that, where the equipment is being modified by the addition of parts, the additions become the Employer's property either when fixed to the equipment (if work is 'off site') or when delivered to Site prior to installation.

   4.1.3   Where the work is undertaken 'off site' in the UK the Contractor should be made responsible for its return to the required Site. Responsibility for off-loading should be agreed prior to delivery.

4.2 Clause 5 – 'Terms of payment'

The terms of payment *must* be specified on the order. The following points should be borne in mind:

4.2.1 Relate time of payment to date of takeover of the equipment by the Employer. It is recommended that some money (retention money) should be retained until the end of the warranty period as 'insurance' against the Contractor not fulfilling his obligations under the contract, eg performance tests, warranty, etc.

4.2.2 Where stage payments have to be agreed these should be related to, and conditional upon, work done. (See also reference to stage payments in note 4.4).
Note: See the provisions of Part One, Section 4, with regard to payments in advance of delivery.

4.2.3 Although it is recommended practice to obtain a 'fixed price', it may be economical in the case of high-value extended-delivery items to agree a price subject to a price adjustment formula. This may work out cheaper than a 'pre-loaded' firm price. In such cases the BEAMA CPA sytem is recommended (see Part One, Section 4).

4.3 Clause 6 – 'Intellectual property rights':

This clause must *not* be altered in any way without legal guidance.

4.4 Clause 13 – 'Warranty period':

This clause defines the Contractor's liabilities during the warranty period. The total claim by the Employer is limited to the restoration of the equipment to full working order, plus reimbursement of any actual losses (excluding profits), including the cost of dismantling and reinstallation, the upper limit of such reimbursement being a sum equal to the full value of the contract. Alternatively the Employer may not accept such a limit and instead require the Contractor to pay all reasonably foreseeable losses.

4.5 Clause 14 – 'Condition of equipment':

Unless the item to be repaired/overhauled has been completely stripped down prior to its tender it is often difficult to establish the exact extent of the work necessary. What may appear to be a fairly straightforward job can often have hidden complications. Such complications may well justify an amendment to the quoted price or, if really serious, may put the viability of the job as a whole in question. This clause sets out the procedure for dealing with such eventualities. Care must be taken to ensure that the problems could not have reasonably been foreseen by the Contractor, before agreeing to amend the price.

4.6   Clause 15 — 'Assignment and sub-letting':
       If it is anticipated that the Contractor intends to sub-let a significant part
       of the work then the details must be discussed and agreed with the
       Contractor before the order is placed.

4.7   Clause 17 — 'Insolvency or bankruptcy':
       The object of this clause is to protect the Employer and allow him to
       retrieve his equipment or free-issue materials should the Contractor find
       himself in financial difficulties. The exercise of the power contained in
       this clause must be carried out as quickly as possible on learning of a
       supplier's financial difficulties as it would not do to let the liquidator,
       administrator or receiver disclaim the contract first. Telexes and telegrams
       should be followed by a confirming letter.

       This clause reflects the new arrangements resulting from the Insolvency
       Act 1985 which introduced the word 'administrative receiver' and the
       'administrator' appointed by a Court. Among the reasons why an
       administrator might be appointed are:

       (a) to continue the company in whole or in part

       (b) to optimise assets for liquidation

4.8   Clause 20 — 'Inspection of Site:
       The Employer has statutory common duty of care towards all persons
       invited on to his property which imposes certain obligations on the
       Employer with respect to their safety. The Occupiers Liability Act 1957
       provides that the Employer may be relieved from some of these obligations
       to the person so invited provided that that person knowingly accepts them.'

       To avoid complications at a later stage it is essential that the Contractor
       visits the Site to examine the equipment and its surroundings; remember
       to specify the person to whom the Contractor should report. The
       discussions, which should be recorded, should highlight any potential
       dangers, eg

       (a) chemical contamination of the equipment (particularly residues) —
           wherever possible it is advisable to clean or purge the equipment
           before handing it over to the Contractor. In any event it is essential
           that the Contractor is made aware of any potential danger.

       (b) where the Contractor has to bring any plant on Site in conjunction
           with the work (eg cranes, fork-lift trucks, etc.) any buried/overhead
           cables, drains, mains or the like must be pointed out.

4.9   Clause 21 − 'Manner of carrying out the Works':
Obviously it would be the Employer's intention to have the work
completed as quickly as possible. Where there are any limitations as to
the hours that may be worked, or to the plant being available to the
Contractor, then these limitations must be discussed and agreed before
the order is placed (see sub-clause 21.2).

4.10   Clause 23 − 'Payments to Site labour':
The Contractor is required to obtain the Employer's approval of his
proposed arrangements for paying his labour, i.e. working hours, rates
of pay, bonuses, etc. These proposals should be made in writing and the
Employer's agreement confirmed in writing either by letter or by inserting
the details in the specification or Purchase Order.

4.11   Clauses 24 to 26 − 'Indemnity/Insurances/Notification':
These clauses set out proposed wording to safeguard the Employer, but
guidance should be sought from one's own broker regarding the value
and extent of the cover required from the Contractor under clause 25.1
(2). However, make sure that the clause 25.2 is put into effect.

4.12   Clause 27 − 'Completion tests and take-over':
This clause sets out the ground rules for conducting the completion tests.
Sub-clause 27.3 has provisions for tests being delayed by the Employer,
eg shortage of feedstock, delays by other contractors, etc.

4.13   Clause 28 − 'Loan of employer's plant and equipment':
Any plant and equipment on hire to the Employer from a third party
must not be loaned to the Contractor as this may invalidate the hire
agreement and put the Employer at risk. No insurance cover is available
for any loss or damage that could occur whilst such plant is being used
by the Contractor.

5. **Overseas application**
These model conditions may be adapted for use with overseas sources of supply
by reference to Part One, Section 9.

Model Eight
General Conditions of Contract
for the Repair or Modification
of Engineering Equipment

1 Definitions

1.1 The term 'Employer' shall mean the company so named in the Employer's Purchase Order.

1.2 The term 'Contractor' shall mean the person, firm or company to whom the Purchase Order is issued.

1.3 The 'Equipment' shall mean the Employer's equipment to be repaired or modified.

1.4 The 'Repaired Equipment' shall mean the Equipment after repairs and/or modifications have been completed in accordance with the Contract shall include such 'free-issue' materials (if any) provided by the Employer as are incorporated therein.

1.5 The 'Plant' shall mean all materials, articles and things of all kinds to be supplied by the Contractor.

1.6 The 'Works' shall mean the work to be done by the Contractor under the Contract and includes all Plant required for that purpose.

1.7 The term 'Purchase Order' shall mean Employer's Purchase Order which specifies that these conditions apply to it.

1.8 'The Contract' shall mean the agreement between the Employer and the Contractor consisting of the Purchase Order, these conditions and any other documents (or parts thereof) specified in the Purchase Order. Should there be any inconsistency between the documents comprising the Contract, they shall have precedence in the order herein listed.

1.9 The 'Contract Price' shall mean the sum named in or ascertained in accordance with the Contract as the contract price, subject to such additions to or deductions from such sum as may be made under the provisions of the Contract.

1.10 The 'Site' shall mean the area of the Employers' premises made available by the Employer to the Contractor for the Works, other than merely for access.

2 Completion date

The date of completion of the Works shall be that specified in the Purchase Order, unless agreed otherwise between the Employer and the Contractor. The Contractor shall furnish such programmes of manufacture and delivery as the Employer may reasonably require and the Contractor shall give notice to the Employer as soon as practicable if such programmes are, or are likely to be, delayed. If the Works includes tests the same shall not be deemed to be completed until such tests have been passed to the reasonable satisfaction of the Employer.

3 Incorrect delivery

All Repaired Equipment shall be delivered at the delivery point specified in the Purchase Order. If any Repaired Equipment is incorrectly delivered the Contractor shall be responsible for any additional expense incurred in delivering it to the correct delivery point.

4 Passing of property and risk

4.1 The Plant shall become the property of the Employer at whichever is the earlier of the following times:

(a) the time when such plant is delivered at the point in the Purchase Order, or

(b) the time when, in pursuance of the Contract, such Plant is fixed to or otherwise made part of the Equipment.

4.2 When the Equipment is removed from the Site the risk in the Equipment shall rest on the Contractor from the time it is handed to the Contractor, his servants or his agents, and shall so remain until the Equipment or the Repaired Equipment is returned to the Employer at the delivery point specified in the Purchase Order.

4.3 The Contractor shall take full responsibility for the Equipment and Plant during the execution of the Contract and in the event of any damage to, or loss of, the Equipment and/or the Plant the Contractor shall repair such damage or make good such loss at the Contractor's own expense, save that where such damage or loss is caused by a defect in the Equipment which could not reasonably have been detected by the Contractor the cost of repairing such damage or making good such loss shall be borne by the Employer.

5 Terms of payment

Unless otherwise stated in the Contract – cash at the close of the month following the month in which the Works are completed. Payment shall only be made after receipt of an invoice. Value Added Tax, where applicable, shall be shown separately on all invoices as a strictly net extra charge.

6 Intellectual property rights

The Contractor will indemnify the Employer against any claim for infringement of patents, registered designs and design rights, trade mark or copyright by anything done by the Contractor hereunder, including the use or sale of any Plant supplied by the Contractor to the Employer, and against all costs and damages which the Employer may incur in any action for such infringement or for which the Employer may become liable in any such action. Provided always that this indemnity shall not apply to any infringement which is due to the Contractor having followed a design or instruction furnished or given by the Employer or to the use of such Plant in a manner or for a purpose, or to any infringement which is due to the use of such Plant in association or combination with any other article or material not supplied by the Contractor. Provided also that this indemnity is conditional on the Employer giving to the Contractor the earliest possible notice in writing of any claim being made or action threatened or brought against the Employer.

7 Force majeure

Neither party shall be liable for failure to perform its obligations under the Contract if such failure results from circumstances which could not have been contemplated and which are beyond the party's reasonable control. Industrial disputes and failures by sub-contractors are not force majeure hereunder.

8 Progress and inspection

The Employer's representatives shall have the right to progress and inspect the Works at all reasonable times and to reject any part thereof that does not comply with the terms of the Contract. The Contractor's sub-contracts shall include this provision. Any inspection, checking, approval or acceptance given on behalf of the Employer shall not relieve the Contractor or his sub-contractors from any obligation under the Contract.

9 Secrecy

No photographs of any of the Employer's equipment, installations or property shall be taken without the Employer's prior consent in writing.
The Contractor shall keep secret and shall not divulge to any third party (except sub-contractors accepting a like obligation of secrecy and then only to the extent necessary for the performance of the sub-contract) all information given by the Employer in connection with the Contract or which becomes known to the Contractor through his performance of work under the Contract.

This undertaking to keep information secret will not apply to information which:

(a) is already in the Contractor's possession prior to its disclosure by the Employer, or

(b) is purchased or otherwise legally acquired by the Contractor at any time from third parties, or

(c) comes into the public domain otherwise than through the fault of the Contractor.

The Contractor shall not mention the Employer's name in connection with the Contract or disclose the existence of the Contract in any publicity material or other similar communication to third parties without the Employer's prior consent in writing.

10 Employer's rights in specifications, plans, drawings, patterns, etc.

Any specifications, plans, drawings, patterns or designs supplied by the Employer to the Contractor in connection with the Contract and intellectual property rights therein are and shall remain the property of the Employer and any information derived therefrom or otherwise communicated to the Contractor in connection with the Contract shall be held by the Contractor as secret and confidential and shall not, without the consent in writing of the Employer, be published or disclosed to any third party, or made use of by the Contractor except for the purpose of the Contract.

11 Responsibility for information

The Contractor shall be responsible for any errors or omissions in any drawings, calculations, packing details or other particulars supplied by him, whether such information has been approved by the Employer or not, provided that such errors or omissions are not due to inaccurate or inadequate information furnished in writing by the Employer. The Contractor shall at his own expense carry out any alterations or remedial work necessitated by reason of such errors or omissions and modify the drawings, calculations, packing details or other particulars accordingly. The performance of his obligations under this paragraph shall be in full satisfaction of the Contractor's liability under this clause but shall not relieve the Contractor of his liability (if any) for failure to complete the Contract within the time stated therein.

12 Free-issue materials

12.1 Where the Employer, for the purposes of the Contract, issues materials free of charge to the Contractor such materials shall be and remain the property of the Employer. The Contractor shall maintain all such materials in good order and condition subject, in the case of tooling, patterns and the like, to fair wear and tear. The Contractor shall use such materials solely in connection with the Contract. Surplus materials shall be disposed of at the Employer's discretion. Waste or loss of such materials arising from bad workmanship or negligence of the Contractor shall be made good at the Contractor's expense. Without prejudice to any other rights of the Buyer, Seller shall deliver up such materials whether further processed or not to Buyer on demand.

12.2 On receipt of such materials the Contractor shall carry out a reasonable visual examination to check that the materials are free from defects or deficiency and accord with the Contract. The Contractor shall notify the Employer as soon as practicable, but within seven days, where any such defects or deficiencies are discovered and the Employer shall replace the materials or make good the deficiencies within a reasonable time of such notice. Any additional costs incurred by the Contractor caused by the failure of the Employer so to do shall be paid by the Employer provided that the Employer shall be under no liability to pay such extra costs if the defect or deficiency was not so notified or arose out of the Contractor's failure to maintain the materials in good order and condition.

13 Warranty period

The Contractor shall as soon as reasonably practicable repair or rectify the Repaired Equipment or any part thereof which is or becomes defective during the period of 12 months from completion of the Works, or take-over (under Clause 27) whichever is applicable, where such defects occur under proper usage and are due to faulty design (other than a design made, furnished or specified by the Employer for which the Contractor has disclaimed responsibility in writing), the Contractor's erroneous instructions as to use or erroneous use data, or inadequate or faulty materials or workmanship or any other breach of the Contractor's warranties, express or implied. Such repairs and rectifications shall themselves be subject to the foregoing obligations for a period of 12 months from the date of completion thereof or passing of tests (if any) whichever is appropriate after repair or rectification. The Contractor shall further be liable in damages (if any) up to the limit of the full value of the Contract provided that the Employer shall not in any event claim damages in respect of loss of profits.

The Contractor shall have no liability for latent defects in free-issue materials. The foregoing states the entire liability in contract and in negligence of the Contractor in respect of defects in the Works other than liability assumed by the Contractor under Clause 24 (Indemnity) and the liability arising in respect of rectification under Clause 27 (Completion tests and take-over), and the Contractor shall not, save as expressly provided herein, be liable for any other claim in regard to defects in the Repaired Equipment.

14 Condition of equipment

If, during the execution of the Contract, it appears to the Contractor that the condition of the Equipment is such that the intent of the Contract is not reasonably practicable, the Contractor shall promptly give the Employer notice in writing to that effect with full particulars of the reasons and the Employer shall within a reasonable time thereafter:

1   instruct the Contractor to continue, add to, alter, omit or otherwise vary the Works and the Contractor shall carry out such instructions and be bound by the same conditions, unless otherwise expressly agreed to in writing, as though the said alterations, omissions or variations were stated in the Contract. The difference in price (if any) shall be determined between the Contractor and the Employer and shall be added to or deducted from the Contract Price; or

2   terminate the Contract and in such event the Contractor shall be entitled to be reimbursed by the Employer for work executed and materials provided up to the date of acceptance by the Employer of the said notice.

15   Assignment and sub-letting

15.1   The Contract shall not be assigned by the Contractor nor shall the Works be sub-let as a whole. The Contractor shall not sub-let any part of the Works without the Employer's written consent, which shall not be unreasonably withheld, but the restriction contained in this clause shall not apply to sub-contracts for materials, for minor details, or for any part of the Works of which the makers are named in the Contract. The Contractor shall be responsible for all work done and materials and articles supplied by all sub-contractors.

15.2   When the Employer has consented to the placing of sub-contracts copies of each sub-order shall be sent by the Contractor to the Employer immediately it is issued.

16   Contractor's default

16.1   If the Contractor fails to carry out promptly any of the Employer's instructions, and fails within ten days of notice by the Employer drawing attention to such failure to take such steps as reasonably satisfy the Employer, the Employer may, without prejudice to any other of his rights, carry out the Works at the risk and expense of the Contractor.

16.2   If the Contractor commits a breach of the Contract and fails within ten days of notice by the Employer to take such steps as reasonably satisfy the Employer to rectify such breach, the Employer may, without prejudice to any other of his rights, terminate the Contract forthwith by notice to the Contractor. Thereupon, without prejudice to any other of his rights, the Employer may himself complete the Works or have them completed by a third party and the Employer shall not be liable to make any further payment to the Contractor until the Works have been completed in accordance with the requirements of the Contract, and shall be entitled to deduct from the Contract Price any additional cost incurred by the Employer. If the total cost to the Employer exceeds the Contract Price, the difference shall be recoverable by the Employer from the Contractor.

17 Insolvency or bankruptcy

If the Contractor becomes insolvent or bankrupt or (being a Company) makes an arrangement with its creditors or has an administrative receiver or administrator appointed or commences to be wound up (other than for the purpose of amalgamation or reconstruction), the Employer may, without prejudice to any other of his rights, terminate the Contract forthwith by notice to the Contractor or any person in whom the Contract may have become vested.

18 General conditions in the tender

No conditions submitted or referred to by the Contractor when tendering shall form part of the Contract unless otherwise agreed to in writing by the Employer.

19 General

19.1 The construction, validity and performance of the contract shall be governed by the laws of England and the parties agree to submit to the exclusive jurisdiction of the English Courts.

19.2 **Notices**

Any notice to be sent under this Agreement should be sent to the addresses given on page one and served personally or by pre-paid registered or recorded delivery letter or fax confirmed by first class post. Letters shall be deemed served 48 hours after posting and faxes on despatch.

19.3 **Waiver**

No delay or omission by Buyer in exercising any of its rights or remedies under this Agreement or under any applicable law on any occasion shall be deemed a waiver of, or bar to, the exercise of such right or remedy or any other right or remedy upon any other occasion.

19.4 **Headings**

The headings in this Agreement are for ease of reference only and shall not affect the construction thereof.

19.5 **Severance**

In the event that any provision of this Agreement shall be void or unenforceable by reason of any provision or applicable law, it shall be deleted and the remaining provisions hereof shall continue in full force and effect and, if necessary, be so amended as shall be necessary to give effect to the spirit of the Agreement so far as possible.

20 Inspection of Site

The Contractor is deemed to have understood the nature and extent of the Works, and to have visited the Site and shall make no claim founded on his failure to do so. The Employer shall, on request of the Contractor, grant such access as may be reasonable for this purpose.

21 Manner of carrying out the Works

21.1 The Contractor shall, on being given possession of the Site, forthwith proceed with the Works and duly complete the same in accordance with the instructions and programme as set out in the Purchase Order.

21.2 The Employer shall use his reasonable endeavours to give the Contractor facilities for carrying out the Works on the Site continuously during the agreed working hours. In the event of a prolonged delay, a reasonable extension of time for completion shall be granted by the Employer.

21.3 The Employer shall have the power at any time during the progress of the Works to order in writing:

(a) The removal from the Site of any materials which are not in accordance with the Contract.

(b) The substitution of proper and suitable materials.

(c) The removal and proper re-execution (notwithstanding any previous test thereof or interim payment therefor) of any work which, in respect of material or workmanship, is not in accordance with the Contract.

21.4 No work shall be laid in excavation and no work shall be covered or hidden until approved by the Employer.

22 Statutory duties and safety

22.1 The Works shall be carried out with the proper regard to health and safety and the Contractor shall observe and conform to all statutory enactments and regulations and any by-laws and/or regulations of local or other authorities applicable to the Works or generally to the Site where the Works are carried out, the cost of supplying and/or doing all things required for the purpose being deemed to be included in the Contract Price. Any additional expenses reasonably incurred by the Contractor in conforming with any such statutory enactments, by-laws and regulations made subsequently to the Contractor's tender shall be added to the Contract Price provided that such additional expenses were not ascertainable at the date of tender.

22.2   The Contractor shall also observe through his staff and work people the 'Works Rules' (available on request) applicable to the Site where the Works are carried out. The Employer shall have the right to require the Contractor immediately on receipt of notice in writing to remove any of his employees on the Site who:

(a) Fails to comply with the Works Rules or

(b) Has, in the opinion of the Employer, misconducted himself, or been negligent or incompetent.

22.3   The Contractor shall be responsible for the suitability and safety of any equipment supplied and used by him and no equipment shall be used which may be unsuitable, unsafe or liable to cause damage. Without lessening the absolute responsibility of the Contractor in regard to such equipment, the Employer shall have the right to inspect such equipment and if, in the reasonable opinion of the Employer, it is unsuitable it shall not be used on the Works, no extra time or costs being allowed for replacement.

23   Payment to Site labour

23.1   The Contractor and his Sub-Contractors (if any) shall pay their respective employees on the Site the rates of wages, and observe hours and conditions of working, recognised by the National Agreements for the industries or trades applicable to the Contractor's work. In the absence of such Agreements the Contractor and his Sub-Contractors shall observe rates and conditions approved by the Employer.

23.2   Bonus and other payments outside those defined in 23.1 above shall be made only in accordance with principles agreed with the Employer.

23.3   Hours of working, including overtime, shall be agreed with the Employer.

23.4   Before the placing of the Contract, the Contractor shall have obtained for himself and his Sub-Contractors (if any) the approval of the Employer for the arrangements covered in 23.1, 23.2 and 23.3 above. The Contractor and his Sub-Contractors shall not introduce or commence to negotiate any changes in these arrangements without the written consent of the Employer. Notice shall be given to the Employer of the implementation of any National Awards affecting these arrangements.

24   Indemnity

The Contractor shall take every practicable precaution not to damage or injure any property or persons. The Contractor shall satisfy all claims founded on any such damage or injury which arise out of or in consequence of any operations under the Contract whether such claims are made by the Employer or by a third party against the Contractor or against the Employer and the Contractor shall indemnify the Employer against all actions, demands, damages, costs, charges and expenses arising in connection therewith provided, however, that nothing in this condition shall render the Contractor liable for any injury or damage resulting from any negligent act or omission of the Employer, his servants or agents, or any other contractor employed by the Employer and the Employer shall indemnify the Contractor against all demands and expenses arising in connection with any such damage or injury.

25 Insurances

25.1 The Contractor shall have in force and shall require any Sub-Contractor to have in force:

(a) Employer's Liability Insurance and

(b) Public Liability Insurance for such sum and range of cover as the Contractor deems to be appropriate but not less than £500,000 for any one accident unless otherwise agreed by the Employer in writing.

All such insurances shall be extended to indemnify the Employer against any claim for which the Contractor or Sub-Contractor may be legally liable.

25.2 The Policy of Insurance shall be shown to the Employer whenever he requests together with satisfactory evidence of payment of premiums.

25.3 The Employer shall maintain Employer's Liability and Public Liability Insurance in respect of his own liabilities.

26 Notification procedure

The Contractor shall give immediate notice in the event of any accident or damage likely to form the subject of a claim under the Employer's Insurance and shall give all the information and assistance in respect thereof that the Employer's insurers may require, and shall not negotiate, pay, settle, admit or repudiate any claim without their written consent, and shall permit the insurers to take proceedings in the name of the Contractor to recover compensation or secure an indemnity from any third party in respect of any of the matters covered by the said insurance.

27 Completion tests and take over

27.1 Completion tests, which shall be in accordance with the provisions of the Contract, shall be made at a time to be agreed with the Employer. The Contractor shall give the Employer seven days' notice of the date after which he will be ready to carry out the tests. If the Employer fails to agree a time or to attend at the time agreed the Contractor shall be entitled to proceed in his absence and the test shall be deemed to have been made in the presence of the Employer.

27.2 When the Works are completed and all completion tests to be made by the Contractor have been passed to the reasonable satisfaction of the Employer, the Employer shall forthwith Take-Over the Repaired Equipment and shall certify accordingly.

27.3 If, by reason of difficulties encountered by the Employer it becomes impossible to proceed with the said completion tests at the agreed time, the Employer shall make payment and Take-Over shall thereupon be deemed to have taken place, provided that the Employer shall not be required to pay at this time the cost of uncompleted work. The Contractor shall, nevertheless, during the Warranty Period carry out the said completion tests when required after reasonable notice from the Employer, and any additional expense incurred by the Contactor shall be repaid by the Employer.

27.4 The Employer may Take-Over any part of the Repaired Equipment whether or not it has passed all its tests and shall certify accordingly in respect of that part.

27.5 The Employer shall be responsible for the care and operation of any part of the Repaired Equipment certified as taken over.

28 Loan of Employer's plant and equipment
(The inclusion of this condition does not imply that the Employer assumes any obligation to provide 'Loaned Plant', which means plant or equipment owned by the Employer and used by or on behalf of the Contractor by agreement.)

28.1 Where Loaned Plant is operated by a servant or agent of the Employer:

(a) The operator shall not become the servant of the Contractor but shall carry out with the Loaned Plant such work as he may be directed to do by the Contractor.

(b) The Contractor shall be liable for any damage to the Loaned Plant caused by misdirection or misuse of it due to negligence on the part of the Contractor, his servants or agents.

(c) The Employer shall be liable for any damage to the Loaned Plant caused by a defect in or faulty operation of the Loaned Plant.

28.2 Where Loaned Plant is operated by a servant of the Contractor or an independent contractor, the Contractor shall be liable for all damage to the Loaned Plant unless he can show that it was caused by a defect present therein at the commencement of the loan and he shall be liable for any loss (including loss by theft) of the Loaned Plant.

28.3 The Employer shall have the right, upon giving reasonable notice to the Contractor, to withdraw Loaned Plant at any time and shall be under no liability whatever in connection with the Employer failing to lend plant at any time.

28.4 The Contractor shall satisfy himself that any Loaned Plant is suitable for the purpose intended.

Guidance notes on the use of Model Nine 'Conditions of Contract for the Hire of Plant (Supplied with Operator)'

1 Use

Use for the hire of Plant which will be driven or operated by employees of the Contractor, eg cranes, excavators, bucket loaders, mobile high pressure water jetting equipment and similar plant. These Conditions are not suitable for off-shore work or for the supply and erection of scaffolding.

2 General note on negotiation

Always specify in the enquiry that it is a condition of the order that these Conditions are to be accepted. If the Contractor raises any objections these can then be the basis for negotiation. Avoid attempting to amend the Contractor's conditions to meet one's own requirements.

3 Definitions of requirements

The following information should be part of any enquiry and/or Purchase Order:

3.1   Quantity, description, specification and duties required.

3.2   Delivery date(s) − be specific.

3.3   Delivery point.

3.4   State what notice and arrangements are required for acceptance of delivery and the 'checking-in' procedures.

3.5   Period of hire − hourly, daily, weekly or monthly.

3.6   Terms of payment.

3.7   Whether hire charge is fixed or subject to variation; if variable define basis.

3.8   Specify what utilities or other facilities will be provided by the Hirer, eg water, electricity, canteen, workshop accommodation, etc.

3.9   Stipulate any restrictions to be imposed on sub-letting (see note 4.4 below).

3.10   Specify insurance cover required.

4 Notes on certain clauses

4.1   Clause 1.5 and Clause 6.2 'Period of Hire':
This definition has been deliberately worded so as to overcome 'double charging' on travelling time.

Where the Plant leaves the Hirer destined for another customer only the charges in respect of the initial journey to the Hirer's Site should be paid. If the Plant returns immediately to the Contractor's depot the Hirer will pay the travelling time in respect of this journey provided that the plant is 'off hire'.

4.2   Clause 2 – 'Inspection of Site':
There is a statutory common duty of care towards all persons invited on to property which imposes certain obligations on the Occupier with respect to their safety. The Occupiers Liability Act 1957 provides that some of these obligations can be transferred to the person so invited, provided that he knowingly accepts them.

To avoid complications at a later stage it is essential that the Contractor visits the Site to discuss all aspects of the Contract. The enquiry should include such an instruction.

The discussions, which should be recorded, should highlight any hidden cables, drains, mains or the like which need to be safeguarded, and any services passing through or over the area of operations.

It is the responsibility of the Hirer to supply and lay suitable timbers or equivalents for heavy plant, eg mobile cranes, to travel over, wherever required by ground conditions, such as shallow buried services, or soft or marshy ground.

4.3   Clause 4 – 'Delivery in good order':
The purpose for which the Plant is to be used must always be stated, as well as the varying circumstances under which the Plant will be expected to operate.

4.4   Clause 8 – 'Assignment and sub-letting':
Any Plant on hire must *not* be loaned to a third party without the Contractor's prior consent in writing, as this will invalidate the Contract. No insurance cover is provided for any loss or damage that could occur whilst the hired Plant is being employed by a third party.

Some owners sub-let the maintenance or inspection obligations of their Contracts. This aspect must be clarified at the enquiry stage, particularly in respect of hires in excess of one month.

4.5   Clause 11 – 'Repairs and adjustments':
Provision must be made for the Contractor to inspect and maintain the Plant. Maintenance of the Plant is solely the responsibility of the Contractor.

In the event of any repairs or adjustments being necessary the lost 'hiring time' resulting from such stoppages is deductable from the hire charge, provided that the repair or adjustment did not result from some act or omission of the Hirer.

4.6   Clauses 13, 14 and 16 – 'Damage to persons or Property/Insurances/ Transportation to and from site:
The Contractor has an unlimited liability in respect of any damage he may cause to the Hirer's property, unless the limit is specified in the Contract. Even then under the Unfair Contract Terms Act 1977 liability for death and personal injury caused by negligence may not be excluded. However, this figure can be reduced in respect of the goods actually being handled (i.e. the 'on-hook' liability in respect of mobile cranes or other lifting appliances) if requested by the Hirer.

Model Nine
Conditions of Contract for
the Hire of Plant (Supplied with Operator)

1 Definitions

1.1 The 'Contract' shall mean the contract between the Hirer and the Contractor consisting of the Hirer's order, these conditions and any other documents (or parts thereof) specified in the Hirer's order.

1.2 The 'Contractor' shall mean the person, firm or company to whom the Hirer's order is issued.

1.3 The 'Hirer' shall mean the company so named in the Hirer's order.

1.4 The 'Operator' shall mean the person or persons in the employment of the Contractor who are assigned to the Plant for the purpose of the Contract. At all times during the Period of Hire the Operator shall be and remain an employee of the Contractor and the Contractor shall be responsible for payment of all wages, National Insurance contributions and other outgoings usually paid by an employer to or on behalf of his employee.

1.5 The 'Period of Hire' shall mean the period commencing when the Plant leaves the Contractor's premises or place where last employed, whichever is the nearer to the Site, and ending upon the removal of the Plant from the Site.

1.6 The 'Plant' shall mean the equipment specified in the Hirer's order and any replacement or replacements thereof, together with such accessories for the same as let by the Contractor to the Hirer.

1.7 'Regulations' shall mean any enactment, order, regulation, or other similar instrument of any Local Authority or Government body, as amended by any subsequent Regulation.

1.8 The 'Site' shall mean the place or places specified at which the Plant is to be employed for the purposes of the Contract.

2 Inspection of Site
The Contractor shall be deemed to have visited the Site and understood the nature

and extent of the work for which the Plant is to be employed and to have willingly accepted all the risks therein. The Hirer shall grant such access as may be reasonable for this purpose. The Hirer shall take all reasonable precautions to ensure that the ground is in a satisfactory condition to take the weight of the Plant and shall, where necessary, supply and lay suitable timbers or equivalents for mobile Plant to travel over.

3 **Delivery of Plant**

3.1   The date of delivery of the Plant shall be that specified in the order unless otherwise agreed in writing between the Hirer and the Contractor.

3.2   If the Plant is incorrectly delivered, the Contractor shall be responsible for any additional expense incurred in delivering it to the correct destination.

4 **Delivery in good order**

4.1   The Contractor shall ensure that the Plant is of sound construction and condition, has been properly maintained, and is in good working order at the commencement of the Period of Hire. In particular the Contractor shall ensure that all provisions of Regulations and British Standard Codes of Practice (where applicable) concerning transportation, construction, maintenance, testing and inspection applicable to the Plant have been complied with and

(a)   shall produce to the Hirer, if so requested, the current certificate of inspection required under any Regulations, and

(b)   shall indemnify the Hirer from liability for any kind of breach of any such Regulations or Codes of Practice.

5 **Loading and off-loading arrangements**
The Contractor shall be responsible for the proper and safe loading and off-loading of the plant at the Hirer's Site and for the provision of all equipment and personnel necessary for this purpose.

6 **Removal of plant, termination and suspension**

6.1   The Contractor shall remove the Plant from the Site with all reasonable speed on receipt of the Hirer's instructions to such effect. In the event that the Contractor fails to remove the Plant from the Site within 24 hours of the date given in such instructions then the Period of Hire shall be deemed to have ended on the date given in the instructions and the Plant shall thereupon become the Contractor's own risk and expense.

6.2   In the event that a hiring to a third party will not commence immediately on conclusion of the Period of Hire, the Hirer will pay the Contractor at the contract rate for the time taken to return the plant to the Contractor's premises, but the Period of Hire shall not thereby be extended beyond the time of removal of the Plant from the Site.

6.3 Notwithstanding the foregoing, the Period of Hire shall be deemed to be suspended from receipt of notice from the Hirer that no Operator is present on the Site to operate the Plant. This notice shall be confirmed later, in writing. If such suspension shall last for one working day the Hirer shall be entitled to terminate the Period of Hire and the Plant shall thereupon become the Contractor's own risk and expense.

7 Identification

The Plant shall at all times remain the property of the Contractor and he shall mark it in such a manner as to make it easily identifiable. Such identification shall not be removed, defaced or covered up by the Hirer.

8 Assignment and sub-letting

8.1 The Hirer shall not transfer possession or lend the Plant or any of the accessories or equipment supplied therewith to any third party unless the Contractor's prior written consent has been obtained.

8.2 The Contract shall not be assigned by the Contractor. The Contractor shall not sub-let any portion of the Contract without the consent in writing of the Hirer, but such consent shall not relieve the Contractor from any obligations under the Contract.

9 Payment

9.1 Unless otherwise agreed in writing, the Contractor shall render invoices at the end of each month for all items of the Plant on hire during that month less any agreed adjustments to the hire charge due in accordance with Clause 11.3.

9.2 Value Added Tax, where applicable, shall be shown separately on all invoices as a strictly net extra charge.

9.3 Unless otherwise agreed in writing, the Hirer shall make payment by the end of the month following the month in which a proper invoice is received by the Hirer.

10 Statutory duties and safety

10.1 The Plant shall be operated only by the Operator and the Contractor shall ensure that such Operator is fully competent.

10.2 All work shall be carried out with proper regard to safety. The Contractor shall observe and conform to all Regulations applicable to the work or generally to the Site where the work is carried out, the cost of supplying and/or doing all things required for the purpose being deemed to be included on the hire charge.

10.3 The Contractor and his employees shall observe the works rules (available on request) applicable to the Site where the work is carried out. The Hirer shall have the right to require the Contractor immediately on receipt of notice in writing to remove, and he shall so remove, any of his employees on the Site who has:

(a) failed to comply with the works rules, or

(b) in the opinion of the Hirer, misconducted himself or been negligent or incompetent.

11 Repairs and adjustments

11.1 If at any time during the Period of Hire the Contractor is of the opinion that the Plant is in need of repair or adjustment the Contractor may stop the use of the said Plant until repairs or adjustments have been made on the Site or, at the Contractor's own expense, supply with all reasonable speed such replacement Plant as is necessary for the purposes of the Contract.

11.2 If at any time during the Period of Hire the Hirer is of the opinion that the Plant is in need of repair or adjustment, the Hirer shall advise the Contractor and may suspend the operation of the Contract until the Contractor has carried out such repairs or adjustments on the Site or has, at the Contractor's own expense, supplied such replacement Plant as is necessary for the purposes of the Contract.

11.3 The hire charge shall be adjusted in proportion to the time lost due to any stoppage or suspension of use of the Plant during the Period of Hire, under the provisions of 11.1 or 11.2 above.

11.4 No adjustment to the hire charge can be claimed where damage as defined in Clause 12 was due to the neglect or default of the Hirer, his servants or agents. However, if the Plant or item thereof is agreed to be beyond repair the Contractor shall with all reasonable speed provide such replacement as is necessary for the purposes of the Contract.

11.5 The Hirer shall at all reasonable times permit the Contractor, his servants, agents or insurers, to have access to the Plant for the purpose of inspecting, testing, adjusting, repairing or replacing the same. Similarly, the Hirer shall permit the Contractor to inspect the work being carried out by the Operator. So far as is reasonably practicable any such inspection etc. shall be carried out at times convenient to the Hirer.

12 Loss or damage to Plant

12.1 The Hirer shall notify the Contractor by telephone or other agreed means immediately in the event of any accident, loss of or damage to the Plant, as well as any breakdown, howsoever caused, for which an adjustment to the hire charge might be claimed in accordance with Clause 11. Such notification shall be confirmed in writing to the Contractor within seven days.

12.2 Where, during the Period of Hire, such loss or damage occurs and is due to the neglect or default of the Hirer, his servants or agents, the Hirer shall pay all reasonable costs incurred by the Contractor in effecting the necessary repairs or, where the Plant or item thereof is agreed by the parties to be beyond repair, shall compensate the Contractor with an amount to be agreed but which shall in no case exceed the market value current at the time for Plant or items thereof of like age and condition.

12.3 The Hirer shall be under no liability for any consequential loss suffered by the Contractor resulting from any accident or damage, howsoever caused.

13 Damage to persons or property

The Contractor shall be responsible for, and shall indemnify the Hirer against, all actions, claims, costs, demands and proceedings in respect of injury to persons or damage to property, including the property of the Hirer, arising out of or in connection with the use of the Plant during the Period of Hire unless such injury or damage shall arise from any act or omission of the Hirer, his servants or agents, or from some breach on the part of the Hirer of his obligations under the Contract.

14 Insurance

The Contractor shall, but without limiting his responsibilities under the Contract, insure against any damage, loss or injury which may occur to any property or any person for which he may be responsible or liable to indemnify the Hirer.

15 Notification of accidents

If the Plant is involved in any accident or other occurrence resulting in injury, loss or damage to persons or property, the Hirer shall give prompt notification thereof to the Contractor.

16 Transportation of the Plant to and from Site

16.1 The Contractor shall use every reasonable means to prevent any loss or damage in respect of the highways or bridges communications with or on the routes to the Site. In particular he shall select routes and use vehicles and restrict and distribute loads so that no loss or damage may result from the use of such highways and bridges.

16.2 The Contractor shall indemnify the Hirer against all claims for loss or damage in respect of any highway or bridge caused by the transportation of the Plant to and from the Site including, without limitation, such claims as may be made by any competent authority directly against the Hirer pursuant to any Act of Parliament or other Statutory Instrument.

16.3 If, notwithstanding 16.1 above, any loss or damage shall occur in respect of any highway or bridge arising from the transportation of the Plant, the Contractor shall notify the Hirer as soon as he becomes aware of such loss or damage or receives any claim in respect thereof.

17 Secrecy

17.1 No photographs of any of the Hirer's equipment, installations or property shall be taken without the Hirer's prior consent in writing. The Contractor, his employees, servants and agents shall keep secret and shall not divulge to any third party any information which is given by the Hirer in connection with the Contract or which becomes known to the Contractor through his performance of the Contract.

17.2 The Contractor, his employees, servants and agents shall not mention the Hirer's name in connection with the Contract or disclose the existence of the Contract in any publicity material or other similar communications to third parties without the Hirer's prior consent in writing.

18 Applicable law
This contract shall be subject to English law and the parties agree to submit to the exclusive jurisdiction of the English Courts.

19 Notices
Any notice to be sent under this Agreement should be sent to the addresses given on page one and served personally or by pre-paid registered or recorded delivery letter or facsimile confirmed by first class post. Letters shall be deemed served 48 hours after posting and facsimiles on despatch.

20 Waiver
No delay or omission by Buyer in exercising any of its rights or remedies under this Agreement or under any applicable law on any occasion shall be deemed a waiver of, or bar to, the exercise of such right or remedy or any other right or remedy upon any other occasion.

22 Headings

The headings in this Agreement are for ease of reference only and shall not affect the construction thereof.

23 Severance

In the event that any provision of this Agreement shall be void or unenforceable by reason of any provision or applicable law, it shall be deleted and the remaining provisions hereof shall continue in full force and effect and, if necessary, be so amended as shall be necessary to give effect to the spirit of the Agreement so far as possible.

Guidance notes on the use of Model Ten 'Model Conditions of Contract for the Hire of Plant (Supplied without Operator)'

1 Use
Use for the hire of Plant which will be used and/or operated by the Hirer:

Machinery such as generators, compressors, pumps, etc.
Fork-lift trucks, roadsweepers and similar mobile plant.
Scaffolding components, for example poles, ladders, cradles, etc., for erection by the Hirer.
Portable buildings, etc.

2 General note on negotiation
Always specify in the enquiry that it is a condition of the order that these Conditions are to be accepted. If the Contractor raises any objections these can then be the basis for negotiation. Avoid attempting to amend the Contractor's conditions to meet one's own requirements (see Part One, Section 1.4).

3 Definition of requirements
The following information should be part of any enquiry and/or Purchase Order:

3.1   Quantity, description, specification and duties required.

3.2   Delivery date(s) − be specific.

3.3   Delivery point.

3.4   State what notice and arrangements are required for acceptance on delivery and the checking-in procedures (see Clause 2).

3.5   Period of hire − daily, weekly or monthly or of fixed-term duration (see Clause 12).

3.6   Terms of payment.

3.7   Whether price of hire is fixed or subject to variation; if variable define basis.

3.8   Request the method of identification of the Contractor's property.

3.9 Whether the plant is subject to the Hirer's inspection prior to delivery.

3.10 Details of Test and/or Certificate of Inspection required under statutory regulations.

3.11 Specify whether the plant is to be used on or across any public highway (see Clause 9).

3.12 In the case of long-term hire specify what utilities or other facilities will be provided by the Hirer, eg workshop accommodation, etc. (see note 4.3 below).

3.13 Stipulate any restrictions to be imposed on sub-letting, eg mainenance, inspection, etc. (see note 4.2 below).

3.14 Specify requirements regarding the removal of plant from site.

4 Notes on certain clauses

4.1 Clause 3 – 'Delivery in good order':
The purpose for which the hired plant is to be used must always be stated as well as the varying circumstances in which the plant will operate. Specify the regulations and British Standard Codes of Practice with which the equipment must comply.

The hours of working, i.e. single shift/double shift, must be stated as this will reflect on the condition of the plant and frequency of maintenance.

4.2 Clause 5 – 'Assignment and sub-letting':
Any plant or equipment on hire must *not* be loaned to a third party (unless, in the case of scaffolding, portable buildings etc., the Contractor's permission has been given in writing). No insurance cover is available for any loss or damage that could occur whilst hired plant is being used by a third party.

Some owners sub-let the maintenance or inspection portions of their contracts. This aspect must be clarified at the enquiry stage and if agreed must be confirmed in writing.

4.3 Clauses 7 and 8 – 'Repair and adjustments/maintenance of plant':
Provision must be made for the Contractor to inspect and maintain the Plant. The responsibility for general maintenance rests with the Contractor, but daily/weekly routine checks, eg tyre pressures, oil and water levels, battery conditions, etc., have to be undertaken by the Hirer.

In the event of any repairs or adjustments being necessary, the lost 'hiring time' resulting from such stoppages is deductable from the hire charge, provided that the repair or adjustment did not result from misuse or damage by the Hirer.

Model Ten
Conditions of Contract for the
Hire of Plant (Supplied without Operator)

1 Definitions

1.1 The 'Hirer' shall mean the company so named in the Hirer's order.

1.2 The 'Contractor' shall mean the person, firm or company to whom the Hirer's order is issued.

1.3 The 'Plant' shall mean the equipment, machinery, tools or portable buildings specified in the order and any replacement or replacements thereof, together with such accessories for the same as let by the Contractor to the Hirer.

1.4 The 'Contract' shall mean the contract between the Hirer and the Contractor consisting of the order, these conditions and any other documents (or parts thereof) specified in the order.

1.5 The 'Site' shall mean the place or places specified in the order to which the Plant is to be delivered.

1.6 The 'Period of Hire' shall mean the period commencing when the Plant is available in condition for use on the Site and ending on the date specified in the order or as otherwise agreed.

1.7 'Regulations' shall mean an enactment, order, regulation, or other similar instrument of any Local Authority or Government body, as amended by any subsequent Regulation.

2 Delivery of plant

2.1 The date of delivery of the Plant shall be that specified in the order unless otherwise agreed in writing between the Hirer and the Contractor. Time shall be of the essence.

2.2 The Contractor shall deliver, off-load and assemble (where applicable) the Plant at the Site. He shall remain responsible for the care and control of the Plant until completion of off-loading and assembly.

2.3 At the time of off-loading the Contractor shall obtain written confirmation from the Hirer of the quantity of Plant delivered. In the event that such confirmation is not obtained the Hirer shall have the right within three days of the date of delivery to notify the Contractor of any item or items omitted from the Plant and the Contractor shall immediately provide any such item at his own expense.

2.4 If the Plant is incorrectly delivered, the Contractor shall be responsible for any additional expense incurred in delivering it to the correct destination.

3 Delivery in good order

The Contractor shall ensure that the Plant is of sound construction and condition, has been properly maintained and is in good working order at the commencement of the Period of Hire. In particular the Contractor shall ensure that all provisions of Regulations and British Standard Codes of Practice (where applicable) concerning construction, maintenance, testing and inspection applicable to the Plant have been complied with and

(a) shall produce to the Hirer, if so requested, the current certificate of inspection required under any Regulations, and

(b) shall indemnify the Hirer from liability of any kind of breach of any such Regulations or Codes of Practice.

4 Identification

The Plant shall at all times remain the property of the Contractor and he shall mark it in such a manner as to make it easily identifiable. Such identification shall not be removed, defaced or covered up by the Hirer.

5 Assignment and sub-letting

5.1 The Hirer shall not transfer possession or lend the Plant or any of the accessories or equipment supplied therewith to any third party unless the Contractor's prior written consent has been obtained.

5.2 The Contract shall not be assigned by the Contractor. The Contractor shall not sub-let any portion of the Contract without the consent in writing of the Hirer, but such consent shall not relieve the Contractor from any obligations under the Contract.

6 Payment

6.1 Unless otherwise agreed in writing, the Contractor shall render invoices at the end of each month for all items of the Plant on hire during that month less any agreed adjustments to the hire charge due in accordance with Clause 7.3. He shall attach thereto a list of the Plant to which the invoices relate in sufficient detail as to enable the Hirer to check the amount due against records kept by him and shall indicate both items returned and those remaining on hire at the end of the month to which the invoice refers.

6.2   Value Added Tax, where applicable, shall be shown separately on all invoices as a strictly net extra charge.

6.3   Unless otherwise agreed in writing, the Hirer shall make payment by the end of the month following the month of presentation of a proper invoice.

7 Repairs and adjustments

7.1   If at any time during the Period of Hire the Contractor is of the opinion that the Plant is in need of repair or adjustment the Contractor may stop the use of the said Plant until repairs or adjustments have been made on the Site, or, at the Contractor's own expense, supply with all reasonable speed such replacement Plant as is necessary for the purposes of the Contract.

7.2   If at any time during the Period of Hire the Hirer is of the opinion that the Plant is in need of repair or adjustment, the Hirer shall advise the Contractor and may suspend the operation of the Contract until the Contractor has carried out such repairs or adjustments on the Site or has, at the Contractor's own expense, supplied such replacement Plant as is necessary for the purposes of the Contract.

7.3   The hire charges shall be adjusted in proportion to the time lost due to any stoppage or suspension of use of the Plant during the Period of Hire, under the provisions of Clauses 7.1 or 7.2 above.

7.4   No adjustment to the hire charge can be claimed where damage as defined in Clause 11 was due to the neglect or default of the Hirer, his servants or agents. However, if the Plant or item thereof is agreed to be beyond repair the Contractor shall with all reasonable speed replace it with plant of similar age and condition for the purposes of the Contract.

8 Maintenance of Plant

8.1   Contractor's obligations. The Contractor shall at his own cost and at all times throughout the Period of Hire:

(a) Provide and maintain the Plant (except as provided for in Clause 8.2).

(b) Ensure that all Regulations regarding the maintenance of the Plant in working order are complied with.

(c) Replace all tyres on mobile Plant as necessary, except where damaged by the act or default of the Hirer.

(d) Repair or replace any Plant becoming unfit for use, provided that the unfitness was not due to any act or default of the Hirer.

8.2 Hirer's obligations. The Hirer shall at his own cost:

(a) Maintain the Plant in clean condition, and take all reasonable precautions to safeguard it and return it to the Contractor at the end of the Period of Hire in the same condition as at the commencement (fair wear and tear excepted).

(b) In the case of powered Plant, unless otherwise agreed in writing, provide fuel, oil and grease and carry out routine maintenance as specified by the Contractor, such routine maintenance to include (where applicable) daily greasing, attendance to water and oil levels, and the maintenance of correct tyre pressures.

(c) In the case of battery-driven Plant, maintain batteries and carry out charging procedures in strict accordance with the manufacturer's instructions.

(d) Provide reasonable facilities during normal working hours for the inspection and servicing of the Plant by the Contractor. Such work, will, as far as possible, be carried out at times convenient to the Hirer.

9 Use of mobile Plant on the public highway

9.1 Mobile Plant shall not be used on any public highway without the Contractor's written consent. If so used, the said Plant shall be licensed by the Contractor at the Hirer's expense. The provisons of this clause shall not apply where notification in writing of such use is given to the Contractor by the Hirer prior to the delivery of the Plant.

9.2 Where mobile Plant is used on the public highway the Hirer shall ensure that the driver holds a current British driving licence applicable to the said Plant.

10 Use of Plant

The Hirer shall:

10.1 Employ an experienced operator (being not less than 18 years of age in the case of mobile Plant) to operate the Plant.

10.2 Not permit the Plant to be overloaded or used for any purpose for which it was not designed or intended.

10.3 Not permit the Plant to be moved from the Site without first obtaining the Contractor's consent, such consent to be confirmed in writing.

10.4 Take all reasonable steps to remain acquainted with the state and condition of the Plant and advise the Contractor forthwith of the suspected development of any faults.

11 Loss of or damage to Plant

11.1 The Hirer shall notify the Contractor by telephone or other agreed means immediately in the event of any accident, loss of or damage to the Plant, as well as any breakdown, howsoever caused, for which an adjustment to the hire charge might be claimed in accordance with Clause 7. Such notification shall be confirmed in writing to the Contractor within seven days.

11.2 Where such loss or damage is due to the neglect or default of the Hirer, his servants or agents, or any other cause except the neglect of or default of the Contractor, his servants or agents, the Hirer shall pay all reasonable costs incurred by the Contractor in effecting the necessary repairs or, where the Plant or item thereof is agreed by the parties to be beyond repair, shall compensate the Contractor with an amount to be agreed but which will in no case exceed the net invoice value paid by the Contractor for the said Plant or item thereof.

11.3 The Hirer shall be under no liability for any consequential loss suffered by the Contractor resulting from any accident or damage, howsoever caused.

12 Termination of hire

Where a fixed Period of Hire is agreed (other than on a daily, weekly or monthly basis) the Hirer shall have the right to terminate the Contract at any time by giving one month's notice in writing to the Contractor. In such event the Hirer shall thereupon pay to the Contractor all moneys then due, and also such additional reasonable costs that the Contractor shall have incurred as a direct result of such termination.

13 Removal of Plant from Site

13.1 The Contractor shall remove the Plant from the Site with all reasonable speed on receipt of the Hirer's written instructions to such effect. In the event that the Contractor fails to remove the Plant from the Site within seven days from the date of such instructions the Hirer shall have the right to return the Plant to the Contractor's premises during the Contractor's normal business hours and to recover the cost of such action from the Contractor.

13.2 The Contractor shall notify the Hirer in writing within seven days of the return of the Plant of any item missing or damaged. Items alleged to be damaged shall be retained, unused, for a further seven days to permit inspection by the Hirer. Compensation for items lost or damaged where agreed by the Hirer shall, subject to the provisons of Clause 11, be paid by the Hirer.

14 Damage to persons or property

The Hirer shall indemnify the Contractor against all actions, proceedings, costs, claims and demands for injury to persons or damage to property arising out of or in connection with the use of the Plant during the Period of Hire unless such injury or damage shall arise from any act or omission of the Contractor his servants or agents, or from some breach on the part of the Contractor of his obligations under the Contract.

15 Insurances

The Contractor shall, but without limiting his responsibilities under the Contract, insure against any damage, loss or injury which may occur to any property or any person for which he may be responsible or liable to indemnify the Hirer.

16 Secrecy

16.1 No photographs of any of the Hirer's equipment, installations or property shall be taken without the Hirer's prior consent in writing. The Contrator, his employees, servants and agents shall keep secret and shall not divulge to any third party any information which is given by the Hirer in connection with the Contract or which becomes known to the Contractor, his employees, servants and agents through his performance of the Contract.

16.2 The Contractor, his servants and agents shall not mention the Hirer's name in connection with the Contract or disclose the existence of the Contract in any publicity material or other similar communications to third parties without the Hirer's prior consent in writing.

17 Applicable law

This contract shall be subject to English law and the parties agree to submit to the exclusive jurisdiction of the English Courts.

18 Notices

Any notice to be sent under this Agreement should be sent to the addresses given on page one and served personally or by pre-paid registered or recorded delivery letter or facsimile confirmed by first class post. Letters shall be deemed served 48 hours after posting and facsimiles on despatch.

19 Waiver

No delay or omission by Buyer in exercising any of its rights or remedies under this Agreement or under any applicable law on any occasion shall be deemed a waiver of, or bar to, the exercise of such right or remedy or any other right or remedy upon any other occasion.

20 Headings

The headings in this Agreement are for ease of reference only and shall not affect the construction thereof.

21 Severance

In the event that any provision of this Agreement shall be void or unenforceable by reason of any provision or applicable law, it shall be deleted and the remaining provisions hereof shall continue in full force and effect and, if necessary, be so amended as shall be necessary to give effect to the spirit of the Agreement so far as possible.

Appendix 1

Model Form
Vendor 'Appraisal'

1 Name of Company and registered Company number:

2 Address (Registered and Head Office):

3 Telephone number:

4 E mail address:

5 Fax number:

6 Local office address:

7 Telex numbers where relevant:

8 Business details (products/services):

9 Manufacturer or agent or licensee:

10 Company status (privately owned, PLC, Ltd):

11 Year when the Company was founded:

12 Chairman:

13 Managing Director:

14 Directors/Local Manager:

15 Company Secretary:

16 Is the Company part of a Group? If so what Group:
(Please send details of Group structure)

17 Company's turnover last year:
(Please send copies of annual reports – last 2 years)

18 Group's turnover last year (if applicable):
(Please send copy of annual reports – last 2 years)

19 Please provide details of work carried out for clients:

20 References:

21 Is the Company registered within ISO 9000:

22 Name of Quality Assurance Manager:

23 Do you hold any other QA clearances eg Ministry of Defence:

24 Are you a manufacturer (fabricator) or stockist or both:

25 Please provide details of range, product size, materials, etc:

26 Please provide details of your facilities (factory size, number of machines, capacity, etc):

27 Please state number of employees (monthly paid and weekly paid):

28 If a stockist please provide size of warehouse and value of stock held:

29 If a contractor providing "services" please state:

(a) Trades and current numbers of weekly staff.

(b) How many do you employ indirectly (ie 714 labour/agency).

(c) Please provide a copy of your tax exemption certificate 714.

(d) Are you a member of any employers associations, is so which.

(e) Do you work in accordance with national agreements, if so which.

(f) Do you have a company safety policy (if so please enclose a copy).

(g) What is your accident frequency rate over the last 2 years.

(h) What was your 'HSE' reportable accident rate last year.

(i) Please provide a copy of your current insurance certificates, covering employer's liability, third party and, if applicable, professional indemnity.

Please complete appraisal by signing (please include title) and dating.
Thank you for your time and kind cooperation.

Appendix 2

Model Form
Vendor 'Assessment'

1   Name of Company:

2   Address visited:

3   Names and titles of representatives at interview:

4   Organisation chart:

5   Essential "out of hours" working contacts (with telephone numbers):

6   Manufacturing capabilities and the equipment employed:

7   To what specification does the Company manufacture (ASTM, DIN, BSI):

8   What work is subcontracted and what are the inspection arrangements for such work:

9   Sources of supply:

10 Does the Company work to a national agreement (for its workforce):

11 Does the Company operate a fixed annual holiday. If so, when:

12 What is the Company's position on union membership:

13 What is the estimate of the current workload:

14 How does the Company respond to an enquiry:

15 How does the Company respond to an order:

16 How does the Company "acknowledge" orders:

17 How does the Company progress orders:

18 Who are the principal clients of the Company:

19 Does reciprocal business exist:

20 Does the Company have accreditation to ISO 9000:

21 Does the Company understand total quality management:

22 Does the Company have a quality training programme:

23 Does the Company have an "approval system" for new suppliers/contractors:

24 Does the Company have an "inspection procedure" for all incoming materials:

25 Does the Company have written Safety, Health and Welfare Procedures:

26 How does the Company comply with COSHH (Substances Hazardous to Health):

27 Have Conditions of Purchase/Contract been agreed:

28 If a Contractor, providing services (work on client's site):

(a) Does the contractor use sub-contractors, if so when:

(b) How does the contractor vet the 'sub-contractor':

(c) Does the contractor have an exemption certificate for the Construction Industry Tax:

(d) What plant and equipment does the contractor own:

(e) What arrangements exist for maintenance inspections of such equipment:

(f) How are sub-contractors managed and their work inspected:

(g) Name, qualifications, training and experience of Safety Manager/Adviser:

(h) What are the contractor's arrangements for Health & Safety Training:

(i) What industrial/protective/safety clothing does the contractor supply to his operatives:

(j) What are the contractor's arrangements for health screening of all new employees:

(k) Has the HSE prosecuted or served prohibition or improvement notices on the contractor during the last two years:

(l) What is the contractor's system for investigating and reporting accidents, disease and dangerous occurrences:

(m) What third-party liability (insurance) cover does the contractor hold:

(n) What experience does the contractor have with the various types of contract. eg lump sum, schedule of rates, time and material, etc:

(o) What are contractor's plant hire rates:

(p) How does the contractor accommodate his personnel/workforce on client's sites:

(q) Does the contractor have a purchasing department:

(r) Does the contractor have special skills/equipment:

(s) What computer software/e-mail facilities does the contractor use:

Appendix 3

Letter of Intent
(Not legally binding)

We have pleasure in informing you that it is our intention to award a contract to

you for ....

generally in accordance with your Tender dated ....

as amplified by your letters dated ....

A formal contract will be issued to you if agreement is reached on the following points:

....

The Contract Price will be ....

Payment will be made in accordance with ....

The limit of Liability under this Letter of Intent is ....

The Conditions of Contract are as detailed in ....

The programme is as follows ....

Insurance requirements are ....

Invoices should be sent to ....

Do not start any work until we have signed the formal contract. Nothing in this letter shall be taken to form a binding legal contract. This document is subject to contract and is not legally binding.

Please acknowledge receipt of this letter:

Yours faithfully,

Appendix 4

Contract Price Adjustment Supplementary Clause and Formulae for use with Home Contracts (including or excluding erection)

Electrical Machinery:
(for which there is no other specific formula)

If the cost to the Contractor of performing his obligations under the Contract shall be increased or reduced by reason of any rise or fall in labour costs or in the cost of material or transport above or below such rates and costs ruling at the date of tender, or by reason of the making or amendment after the date of tender of any law or of any order, regulation, or by-law having the force of law in the United Kingdom that shall affect the Contractor in the performance of his obligations under the Contract the amount of such increase or reduction shall be added to or deducted from the Contract Price as the case may be provided that no account shall be taken of any amount by which any cost incurred by the Contractor has been increased by the default or negligence of the Contractor. For the purposes of this clause "the cost of material" shall be construed as including any duty or tax by whomsoever payable which is payable under or by virtue of any Act of Parliament on the import, purchase, sale, appropriation, processing or use of such material.

The operation of this Clause is without prejudice to the effect if any which the imposition of Value Added Tax or any tax of a like nature may have upon the supply of goods or services under the Contract.

Variations in the cost of materials and labour shall be calculated in accordance with the following Formula:

(a) Labour
The Contract Price shall be adjusted at the rate of 0.475 per cent of the Contract Price per 1.0 per cent difference between the BEAMA Labour Cost Index for Electrical Engineering published for the month in which the tender date falls and the average of the Index figures published for the last two-thirds of the Contract Period, this difference being expressed as a percentage of the former Index figure.

(b) Materials

The Contract Price shall be adjusted at the rate of 0.475 per cent of the Contract Price per 1.0 per cent difference between the Table 3 Producer Price Index Numbers of materials and fuel purchased 1980 SIC 3420 Basic Electrical Equipment last published in th Government Journal "British Business" before the date of tender and the average of the Index Figures commencing with the Index last published before the two-fifths point of the Contract Period and ending with the Index last published before the four-fifths point of the Contract Period, this difference being expressed as a percentage of the former index figure. (The following footnotes must be added as appropriate according to whether the Contract excludes or includes erection).

For Contracts Excluding Erection

For the purpose of this formula:

(i) Where separate portions of the plant are ready for despatch at different times and are invoiced separately, the Contract Price shall, in relation to each such portion, be an appropriate proportion of the total Control Price.

(ii) The Contract period in respect of the Plant or any portion thereof shall be that period between the date of order and the date ("the completion date") when the Plant or such portion is ready for despatch, or such short period (ending at the completion date) corresponding to the manufacturing cycle of the Plant or such portion as may be agreed in the Contract.

(iii) Where any Index figure is stated to be provisional or is subsequently amended, the figure shall apply as ultimately confirmed, or amended.

Basic Claim for Contract-Price Adjustment

Customer . .*A.N. EXAMPLE*. . . . Customer's Order No . . . .

A. Contract Price *£17,750*

B. Tender or Cost Basis Date . . . . *16 September 1996*

C. Date of Order . . . . *22 October 1996*

D. Date when ready for despatch/Taking over . . . . *2 November 1997*

E. Contract Period between C and D Days . . . . *77 Days*

F. Date at one-third of Contract Period . . . . *25 February 1997*

G. Date at two-fifths of Contract Period . . . . *21 March 1997*

H. Date at four-fifths of Contract Period . . . . *19 August 1997*

I. Labour Cost Index at Tender or Cost Basis Date *163.9*

J. Average of Labour Cost Indices for period F to D *174.4*

K. Department of Trade and Industry Figures or Materials for

   *Basic Electrical Equipment/Mechanical Engineering last

   published before Tender or Cost Basis Date *118.2*

L. Average of Department of Industry Index figures commencing with

   Index last published before date at G and ending with the

   Index last published at H *24.8*

M. **Labour Adjustment** $47.5 \times \dfrac{J - I}{I} = \dfrac{10.5 \times 47.5}{163.9} =$ 3.0430%

N. **Material Adjustment** $47.5 \times \dfrac{L - K}{K} = \dfrac{6.6 \times 47.5}{118.2} =$ 2.6523%

P. **Total Percentage Adjustment for Labour and Materials**   =   5.6953%

Total Price Adjustment

$$= A \times \dfrac{P}{100} = £17,750 \times \dfrac{5.6953}{100} \quad 3 \quad £1010.92$$

* Delete as appropriate

Appendix 5

Activities & Requirements/Information

| Project plan | Contract pla|

● **Project plan**
- Identify contract activities/work
- Plan contract prepn & work
- Budget for work
- Resource contract prepn.
- Contract policy/ strategy
- Interfaces – specialist engs
           work location
- Contract system/procedures
- Financial influences grant

● **Contract plan**
- Define scope of work
- Devise overall work schedule
- Budget availability & phasing
- Contract resource obtained
- Contract policy
- Define   design
  interfaces other projects
  consult   elect/instrume
           fire protn
           other modules
           p lines
           etc.
- Contractor initial screening

- Tender evaluation criteria/principles

Start — Project plan — Update project plan — Contract plan — 1-2 weeks

Appendix 6
CIPS Model Conditions of Contract

The Chartered Institute of Purchasing and Supply issues the following Model Forms of Conditions of Contract, available from CIPS Bookshop, Easton House, Easton on the Hill, Stamford, Lincs. PE9 3NZ. Telephone 01780 756777, Fax 01780 751610.

Computer and Telecommunications Equipment and Services

Model Forms of Conditions of Contract and Guidance Notes designed for use by buyers and sellers. Avoid later contractual disputes and reduce time spent in negotiation.

* 10% discount is given when buying 6 or more.   * Licensing negotiable

These are single usage models protected by copyright.

1	For the Supply and Installation (Purchase) of Computer Equipment	£8.95
2	For the Servicing (Maintenance) of Computer Equipment	£8.95
3	For the Hire and Servicing (Maintenance) of Computer Equipment	£8.95
4	Licence Agreement for the Use of Computer Software Products (inc. Trial Agreement)	£8.95
5	For Software Development	£8.95
6	For the Support and Maintenance of Bespoke Software	£8.95
7	For the Supply and Installation (Purchase) of Telecommunication Equipment	£8.95
8	For the Servicing (Maintenance) of Telecommunications Equipment	£8.95
9	For the Supply and Installation (Purchase) of Second-User Computer and Telecommunications Equipment	£8.95
10	For the Hire of Computer Staff (September)	£8.95
11	For the Supply of Computer Facilities Management Services	£7.95
12	For Turnkey Computer Contracts	£10.95

Model Conditions of Contract when using the Services of a Travel Agent	£5.00
Model Conditions for the Carriage of Goods by Road in the UK 1990 (CIPS and FTA)	£1.50 *to cover p&p*
Model Conditions for the Supply of Liquid Fuels	£5.00
Model Form of Conditions of Contract Confidentiality Agreement	£7.95
Model General Conditions of Purchase for Universities and other Institutions of Higher Education	£8.95

Index